C000241563

Other Titles of Interest

Also of Interest

LOUDSPEAKERS
FOR
MUSICIANS

by

Vivian Capel

BERNARD BABANI (publishing) LTD
THE GRAMPIANS
SHEPHERDS BUSH ROAD
LONDON W6 7NF
ENGLAND

Please Note

Although every care has been taken with the production of this book to ensure that any projects, designs, modifications and/or programs etc. contained herewith, operate in a correct and safe manner and also that any components specified are normally available in Great Britain, the Publishers do not accept responsibility in any way for the failure, including fault in design, of any project, design, modification or program to work correctly, or to cause damage to any other equipment that it may be connected to or used in conjunction with, or in respect of any other damage or injury that may be so caused, nor do the Publishers accept responsibility in any way for the failure to obtain specified components.

Notice is also given that if equipment that is still under warranty is modified in any way or used or connected with home-built equipment then that warranty may be void.

First Published – March 1991
Reprinted – May 1994
Reprinted – May 1997

British Library Cataloguing in Publication Data

Capel, Vivian

Loudspeakers for musicians

1. Loudspeakers

I. Title

621.38284

ISBN 0 85934 242 5

Cover Design by Gregor Arthur

Printed and bound in Great Britain by Cox & Wyman Ltd, Reading

About the Author

His work as an audio, television and radio engineer with several service organisations including that of Philips, gave him a wide experience expanded by his practical and advisory work on large public address systems. As a violinist who has played in several amateur orchestras, he is able to combine the viewpoint of both technician and musician.

His articles have appeared in the technical press for over thirty years, and he is the author of a dozen books on audio, acoustics and related subjects. He now works full time as a writer and audio consultant.

Acknowledgements

The Author and Publishers of this book would like to thank Celestion International Ltd for their kind permission in allowing a number of their enclosure designs to be included in this book.

Preface

Few musicians can claim also to be sound technicians. Their scene is making music, not delving into the technicalities of the complex equipment that nowadays is needed to produce it.

Yet the high cost of equipment makes the prospect of constructing your own very attractive. With the electronic gear there is little that can be done in the way of DIY unless you are one of the knowledgeable few. Loudspeakers though, are a different story. You can save a lot by building your own, and it doesn't need an electronic genius to do it. Ten designs are included at the end of this book which should give results equally as good as commercial ones at a fraction of the cost.

But to blindly construct from a plan is not the best way, far better it is to have some idea of what you are doing, and why you are doing it. An insight into why loudspeakers sound the way they do will help you pick the right design and also guide experiments to get the sound you want.

Much of the problem in understanding things technical is because the language of music and technology is so different. The musician talks about semitones, tones and octaves, the technician about frequencies and wavelengths; the musician listens to a sound's timbre and tone quality, while the technician measures its harmonic content.

So, as we explore the nature of sound, examine the various features of loudspeaker drivers, delve into crossover networks, investigate the different types of cabinets, find out why wadding is used, and consider some actual designs, we relate the technical jargon to musical terms. Although technical terms must of necessity be used, they are explained to make them clear to a non-technical reader. This is a loudspeaker book written especially for working musicians.

Vivian Capel

Contents

Chapter 1

SOUND OF MUSIC

What is sound? What is music? The first question is a lot easier to answer than the second. Sound is often described as a series of waves in the air. This is quite correct but needs qualifying. First, sound can be transmitted through many mediums other than air, but for our purposes we will consider air as the principal one.

The term *wave* although correct can be misleading. We usually think of waves as those seen at the seaside, vertical displacements of water consisting of ridges separated by troughs. We would probably define a wavy line as one that changed direction up and down in a more or less regular fashion throughout its length.

Sound waves, although behaving in a similar manner to sea waves or ripples on water in the way they are propagated, diffracted and reflected, are not vertical variations but consist of backwards-and-forwards motions of the air particles. These produce successive regions of compression and expansion or pressure differences, which spread outward from the source.

Air is a springy material, as anyone who has tried to operate a blocked air pump will have discovered, so the progress of sound waves can be illustrated by imagining a long coiled spring supported at its ends. A series of longitudinal impulses applied at one end travel along it as a train of compressions and expansions between the individual coils as shown in Figure 1.

Just as the coils of the spring do not travel from one end to the other but move backwards and forwards, so the air particles themselves do not move outward from the source, but each imparts oscillatory motion to the next.

The pressure waves of the original sounds are picked up by a microphone which produces corresponding voltage variations. These are then amplified to produce the current to drive the loudspeaker. Now as the voltage generated by the microphone rises and falls, it can best be represented by a wavy line, in

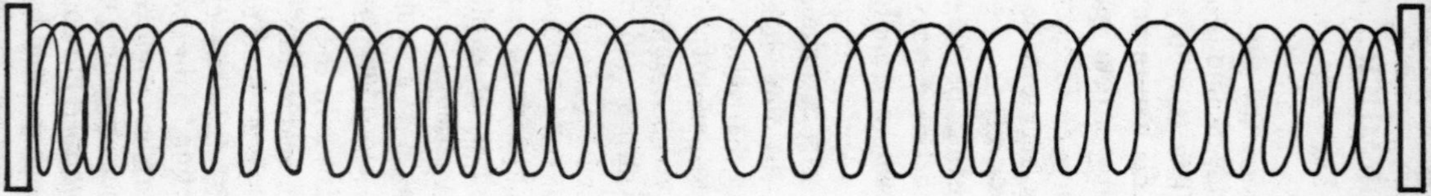

Fig. 1. A sound wave travels through air like a compression wave along a spring, producing travelling regions of high and low compression.

other words, a wave of more conventional appearance. This is how it appears on the screen of an instrument known as an oscilloscope. In this form, experts can easily pick out various forms of distortion and can measure and compare the height or amplitude of the wave with that of others. It would be very difficult to visually analyse a wave if represented by regions of varying pressures, in fact it would be difficult to depict it at all on a two-dimensional screen.

So then, although sound waves consist of pressure differences producing fore-and-aft air particle motion, they are normally represented when converted to electrical signals, by conventional lateral waveforms. This is how they will be depicted as we proceed.

Wavelength and Frequency

Wavelength is obviously the distance from the crest of one wave to that of the next − or for that matter any part of a wave to the corresponding part of its successor. When a series of waves is travelling through a medium at a fixed speed we can count the number of waves that pass a given point in a given time. This we term the *frequency*. If the wavelength is short, there are many waves in a given area, and a large number pass the given point in the specified time. If though the wavelength is long, say twice as long as before, there will be only half as many waves in that area and only half the number will pass the point in the same time.

So there is a definite relationship between wavelength and frequency; as the wavelength gets shorter, the frequency increases proportionately. Sounds that are low in frequency are those produced in the bass register of musical instruments. These have long wavelengths. Those in the treble register are of high frequency and have short wavelengths.

Coming now to the technical terms used to describe these, frequency was once specified by the term *cycles-per-second* (c/s) and the multiple was the kilo; the *kilocycle-per-second* being a thousand c/s. This has now given way to the *hertz* (Hz) a less clumsy but also less obvious unit until you get used to it. The multiple is the *kilohertz* (kHz).

Wavelength has no unit other than physical length, usually expressed metrically. So we say that a certain sound frequency

3

has a wavelength of so many metres, or if a high frequency, so many centimetres. It is often depicted by the Greek letter lambda (λ).

It should be noted that the relation between a particular frequency and its wavelength is governed by the speed of the wave through the medium. For sound this is 1,120 ft per second or 341 metres per second. This figure is for a temperature of 60°F (15.5°C); it increases by 2 ft per second for a temperature rise of each degree C. It is also affected by barometric pressure, but the effect is much less.

This explains why the pitch of a wind instrument changes with temperature as the natural wavelength of the tubes produce a different frequency at different temperatures.

Frequency and Pitch
How then does all this relate to the musical scale? Various standards of pitch have been used over the years. The Standard pitch was one used for most domestic music making, and most parlour pianos were tuned to it. Concert pitch, preferred by professionals, was a semitone higher. The problems can be imagined when a number of players got together for a performance and found that their instruments were tuned to different pitches. Usually everyone had to tune to the piano if there was one. If it was Continental pitch, wind instruments tuned to Concert pitch often couldn't make it, and although strings could be tuned a whole tone down, they often went quickly out of tune afterwards with dire effects on the music making.

Fortunately, what was called Concert pitch has now become the standard. The frequency of middle C is set at 261 Hz, and A at 440 Hz.

Octaves
When successive notes spaced an octave apart are played, the spacing between them sounds equal, and it could be assumed that each octave covers the same number of frequencies. This is not so. Each octave is *double* the frequency of the one below it. Thus middle C is 261.6 Hz; C^1 is 523.2 Hz; C^2 is

4

1,046.4 Hz; C^3 is 2,092.8 Hz; and C^4 is 4,185.6 Hz. In descending order from middle C, C_1 is 130.8 Hz; C_2 is 65.4 Hz; and C_3 is 32.7 Hz.

Thus the rather surprising fact emerges that the top octave is equal in its range of frequencies to all the lower octaves put together.

The perfect diatonic scale (that is the eight notes of the octave) consist of intervals that are sub-multiples of the key note and so are all harmonious with it. Starting from C as the key note, the intervals ascend in the ratios: 1.125 (D); 1.25 (E); 1.333 (F); 1.5 (G); 1.666 (A); 1.875 (B); and 2.0 (C).

There is a snag though. With these ratios, that between the second and third notes, D and E, is 1.25/1.125 which is 1.111. So if we use D as our key note of an ascending scale, the first interval is different from the first interval when C is the key note, namely 1.125. This applies to most of the other intervals and also when using other key or starting notes. So, a piece of music composed in one key could never be transposed to a different key without sounding out of tune.

The remedy is to compromise or temper the scale. Instead of harmonically relating all the notes of a scale to its key note, each is related to its predecessor in the chromatic scale (the twelve notes including semitones). The ratio is a mathematical rather than a harmonic one, and is 1.059464. So if a frequency is multiplied by 1.059464 twelve times it is doubled, thereby spanning the octave.

This is known as the tempered scale and is the one to which all instruments are now tuned, at least those in the Western world. As a result, musical compositions can be transposed to any other key. This is essential for modern orchestral playing as many of the orchestral instruments have a natural pitch other than C. The orchestral clarinet is pitched in B flat and the French horn in F, so these must be transposed either by the players as they go along or on the printed score. When the score is transposed it seems as though these instruments are playing in a different key from everyone else!

Most of the eight notes of the tempered diatonic scale are very close in frequency to those of the perfect harmonic scale as can be seen from the chart on page 6, some are a little above

5

and others a little below. A and B are the furthest.

Note	Harmonic Ratio	Perfect Scale	Tempered Scale
		Hz	Hz
C	1.0	261.6	261.6
D	1.125	294.3	293.6
E	1.25	327.0	329.6
F	1.33	348.8	349.2
G	1.5	392.4	391.9
A	1.66	436.0	440.0
B	1.875	490.5	493.8
C^1	2.0	523.2	523.2

*Frequency Ratios of Perfect Diatonic Scale of C
with Tempered Scale*

Loudness and Pitch

A phenomena which is not widely known yet which was noted as far back as 1935 is that pitch changes with loudness, and the amount and direction depends on frequency. At around C^2 (1,046.4 Hz) there is no change, but an octave higher, (C^3) at above 70 dB, the pitch sharpens by some half a semitone, and sharpens further as the volume increases. At C^4 which is top C, the pitch sharpens by more than a semitone, and at higher volumes above 80 dB can approach a whole tone sharp.

Below C^2, the pitch flattens with an increase in volume. At middle C, the pitch is around half a semitone flat at 70 dB, and a semitone at 85 dB. At C_1, the effect is even more pronounced with the pitch falling a semitone at 70 dB, and a whole tone at 85 dB.

It is evident from this that music played very loud will be discordant, with the treble being sharpened and the bass flattened. With electronic instruments, the performers may be unaware of this as they will not be in the direct line of fire of the main audience loudspeakers, but hearing the result from monitors on stage playing at a much lower level. Such a lower level will be essential if there is a vocalist to avoid feedback.

The bass instruments could be tuned somewhat sharp and the treble flattened slightly to minimise the effect, but then this would sound wrong on the monitors. It would probably be best to leave the treble instruments as they are but sharpen the bass ones; better still, play at a more moderate level.

Loudness and Hearing

The ears do not respond in a linear manner to changes in volume. They have built-in 'automatic volume controls' that turn down as the volume is increased. This enables us to hear very faint sounds at maximum sensitivity, and also very loud sounds without distortion. The ear can handle a range of sound pressures of up to one million times the difference between the faintest and loudest sounds which is far greater than any microphone could cope with. The response to increasing sound levels cannot therefore be linear, but proceeds in a logarithmic fashion.

The unit used to specify sound levels is the decibel (dB) which is logarithmic. It is not strictly a unit of sound but one of comparison, it describes the ratio between two sound, voltage or power levels. In the latter case they are used for specifying the gain of amplifiers, the output compared to the input. Some common values are: 6 dB ×2; 10 dB ×3; 14 dB ×5; 20 dB ×10; 40 dB ×100; 60 dB ×1,000.

Note that by adding the dB values, the ratios are multiplied, thus 20 dB + 40 dB = 60 dB which is 10 × 100 = 1,000. When used to describe sound levels, dB values are related to the level which is taken as the threshold of human hearing, that is the lowest level that a person with good hearing can detect. This is a level of 20 millionths of a Pascal (the Pascal is the present unit of pressure, but others have been used in the past). The suffix A is often added to denote that the measurement is adjusted to compensate for the uneven frequency response of the ears.

This threshold is given the value of 0 dB. A whisper at 1 metre is about 50 dBA; a good speaking voice at the same distance about 70 dBA; a vacuum cleaner around 80 dBA; a

7

symphony orchestra playing *fff* 90 dBA; discos around 100 dBA; pneumatic drill at 1 metre, 110 dBA; a jet aircraft taking off 125 dBA. A level of 130 dBA is the maximum above which permanent damage to the delicate hearing mechanism can rapidly occur.

Damage can occur at lower levels if exposure is prolonged. Hence exposure times are regulated in industry. The maximum permitted time for an exposure to 99 dBA is 1 hour; to 102 dBA is 30 minutes; to 105 dBA it is 15 minutes; to 108 dBA it is just 7.5 minutes; and to 111 dBA it is only 3.75 minutes.

The resulting damage from over-exposure is not immediately apparent as it affects only the higher frequencies. Victims can hear low pitched sounds as well as before, but lose the highs. A common effect is that speech can be heard but not understood because the parts of speech which make it intelligible, the consonants, are conveyed by the higher frequencies; so speech just sounds a mumble. The effects get progressively worse with continued exposure.

There is then very good reason for public performers on electronic instruments and disco operators to take a responsible attitude and keep the volume moderate. The discords previously mentioned will also thus be avoided.

Harmonics

The question is sometimes asked as to why the various musical instruments sound different when playing the same notes. How do our ears distinguish them, and how is that difference conveyed by the loudspeakers.

Part of the reason is that very few instruments produce a pure tone of just the frequency of the note being played. The flute playing in its higher registers is the most notable exception. All others generate other frequencies which mostly are multiples of the basic note which is termed the *fundamental*. These multiples are called harmonics.

For convenience these are numbered according to the multiple they are, thus twice the fundamental is called the second harmonic; three times, the third; four times, the fourth; and so on. The slightly confusing aspect of this is that the first actual harmonic encountered ascending from the fundamental is thereby termed the second, and the second encountered is called the third. However, as it is more logical to match the name of the harmonic to the number of the multiple the convention stands. One can avoid the confusion by thinking of the fundamental as the first harmonic.

Each instrument generates a different set of harmonics and in different proportions. Other frequencies are often also produced from various parts of the instrument which are not multiples of the note being played; these are called *overtones* although the harmonics are also often referred to as overtones. This combination of frequencies produces a characteristic timbre or tone quality which distinguishes the instrument from all other kinds.

Analysis of the harmonic content of particular instruments reveals in almost every case that the harmonics and their proportion change over the instrument's range, and also differ according to whether the instrument is played loudly or softly. Usually, there are more harmonics generated in the bass register, and when the instrument is played loudly.

This adds to the variety of musical sound, as variations in loudness thereby produce subtle tonal differences as well as the obvious difference in volume. Expressiveness is thus achieved, yet much of modern music is played at constant volume – very loud – so sacrificing much of the expression which is the very heart of music.

Transients

Not all of the individuality of particular kinds of instruments is conveyed by the harmonics and overtones. Much also depends on the way notes start, develop and end. Notes played on a percussive instrument such as the piano or guitar, start abruptly at high volume and die away gradually. Wind instruments start more gently and can maintain or even increase their volume throughout the length of the note. The start of each note contains rapid high-frequency components which are called *transients*, and these, as well as the way the notes terminate, contribute much to the characteristic sound of the instrument.

Some years ago the author conducted an experiment with a small orchestra in which he played. Each instrument played a scale which was recorded. The recording was then 'topped and tailed' by erasing the start and finish of each note leaving only the centre portion. The tape was then played back to the performers who had recorded it, and each had to write down which scales were played by which instruments. No-one had 100% correct and many had less than 50%. It was very difficult to identify the instruments without the familiar starting and finishing sounds.

Resonance

Every physical body has a particular frequency at which it will readily vibrate when stimulated. This is termed its *resonant frequency*, and usually the vibrations are accompanied by harmonics. The body will also vibrate at other frequencies, but these are less pronounced. Loudspeaker cones, wooden panels and even enclosed areas of air have their particular resonant frequency which depends on the mass and size of the object.

When music is being reproduced from a hi-fi loudspeaker, resonances emphasize one particular frequency and so give an unnatural and often unpleasant effect. Resonances play a significant part in loudspeaker design. With acoustic musical instruments though, various air and panel resonances are used and carefully controlled by the maker to give richness and timbre to the sound. So one's attitude to resonance depends on whether you are producing music or re-producing it.

Having explored briefly the technical terms and jargon associated with sound and acoustics and how they relate to musical performance, we will take a look at the heart of the loudspeaker, the moving coil driver, in the following chapter.

Chapter 2

THE LOUDSPEAKER DRIVER

When does a piece of paper sound like a piano, or a guitar, or a bass drum, or a whole orchestra? The answer is: when it is a loudspeaker cone. We are surrounded by loudspeakers of every size and for every purpose, so we tend to take them for granted. Yet when we consider that they can reproduce any sound that can be heard by the human ear, their ability is seen to be truly remarkable.

How do they do it? Well, we saw in the preceding chapter that all sound is a series of compression and expansion waves of various wavelengths. The loudspeaker cone is made to move forward and backward in sympathy with the microphone diaphragm that picked up the original sounds. When it moves forward it compresses the air in front of it, and when it moves backward it rarefies or expands it. Thus it produces replicas of the original sound waves, reproducing their comparative intensity and frequency. So the sounds produced by a top grade loudspeaker system are almost indistinguishable from the originals.

A question that is somtimes asked though is how can a single cone reproduce two or more different instruments simultaneously? How can the cone move in different directions and at different frequencies at the same time? Of course it cannot, but it doesn't have to.

What happened originally was that the two or more waves combined to form a *resultant*. This is illustrated in Figure 2. Here we see two waves of different frequencies, but the third wave is the addition of the other two. It is formed graphically by simply measuring the height of each at the same point in time, and plotting the sum. These plots are then joined up to form the resultant wave.

This resultant actuated the microphone diaphragm and thereby also the loudspeaker cone. Our eardrums respond to it, but it is the brain that sorts it all out, analysing the resultant and recognizing the two original sounds.

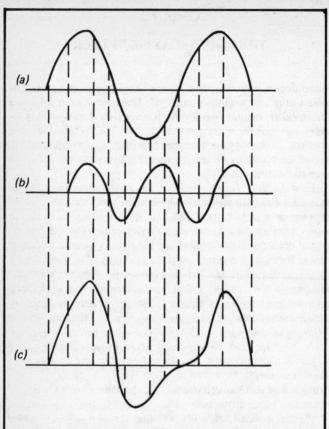

Fig.2. Two or more waves (a and b), can be combined into a single wave (c), by adding instantaneous positive and negative values. This is known as a resultant, and is the way a loudspeaker cone moves to produce multiple waves.

The resultant wave of a full orchestra and choir playing a tutti is indeed complex, but it is nevertheless conveyed by a single motion of the loudspeaker cone. Of course the really miraculous part is played by our brain which can distinguish the many different instruments, voices, and notes from the apparent jumble of that resultant wave.

The same principle applies when the loudspeaker is used to produce original sounds rather than reproduce ones made elsewhere. Vibrating electric guitar strings do not generate sound directly but instead, an electrical waveform, which when amplified, produces cone movement of the loudspeaker. This radiates sound waves which correspond closely to the string vibrations.

Electronic keyboard instruments have no vibrating parts but have oscillators that generate electrical waveforms at frequencies corresponding to those of the standard musical scale, and with a pattern of harmonics and overtones that can be varied by controls on the instrument. No sound or even physical vibrations are produced, so the loudspeakers generate sounds that have not before existed, from the electrical signals.

Although capable of such remarkable feats of production and reproduction, the moving-coil loudspeaker is not a complicated device, but quite simple in operation. As with many simple concepts though, there is more to it than meets the eye in detail. Seemingly quite minor details can make a considerable difference in performance.

We will then explore the driver part by part to see just what is involved and how they affect the resulting sound. A cross section of a typical unit is shown in Figure 3.

Cone Surround

The cone is usually made of paper and is fixed around its outer edge to the frame either directly or by means of a flexible roll of cloth, sponge or rubber. The roll can be either a *half-roll out* in which the roll faces outward or a *half-roll in* whereby it faces inward toward the back of the speaker. When the cone is fixed directly to the frame, there are corrugations around the perimeter; these can be of *two sine rolls*, a *single sine roll* or a deeper *accordion pleat.*

The purpose of these is to permit forward and backward motion of the cone while holding it firmly against any sideways movement, but they also have another important function. When the cone vibrates, ripples can spread out from the centre like ripples in a pond when a stone is thrown in.

13

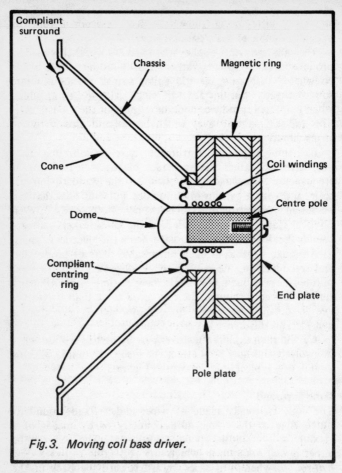

Fig. 3. Moving coil bass driver.

If you observe pond ripples closely, you will notice that if they encounter a hard boundary such as a stone sidewall, they are reflected back across the surface, but if they meet a soft perimeter of reeds, grass or mud, they are mostly absorbed and very few are reflected.

In the case of the loudspeaker cone, reflections produce spurious cone motion that is not in response to any electrical output from the amplifier. So a necessary function of the

14

surround in a hi-fi loudspeaker is to absorb and dampen such vibrations, so preventing reflections. When the surround is of pleated paper, i.e. an extension of the cone itself, there are many such reflections. While this is undesirable for a hi-fi loudspeaker, it is often preferred for lead or rhythm guitar use as it results in a bright 'zingy' tone. The cloth surround gives a smoother response and better bass and so is often the choice for the bass instruments. Rubber gives the least coloured sound and is the best for vocals, monitors and hi-fi.

Cone Materials

If ripples and flexures which can colour the reproduction even before they may be absorbed by the surround, are to be avoided, the cone should be made as stiff as possible. When a pond surface is frozen hard, ripples, waves or any other disturbances are not possible. Similarly, a perfectly stiff cone would move like a piston, backwards and forwards without any flexures, and so should radiate air pressure waves that are a perfect replica of the electrical currents flowing through the speaker circuit.

So why not make the cone of metal such as aluminium? They have, but that exchanges one set of problems for another. Metal cones tend to 'ring' when subject to vibration, like a bell when it is struck. Most hollow metal cans or boxes give a distinctive sound when flicked with a striker such as a pencil. An ideal loudspeaker cone should have no sound of its own at all, if it has, it will colour the sound it reproduces.

Another problem is inertia. The loudspeaker cone must accelerate and de-accelerate very quickly in order to produce the very fast vibrations that make up a complex sound wave. To do this its mass must be low. A motor bike will always be away quicker from the lights than an articulated lorry in spite of having a much smaller engine, because its mass is a tiny fraction of that of the lorry. Metal cones, even aluminium ones, are much heavier than other materials commonly used, so they have a disadvantage here too. Honeycombed aluminium is light and about a thousand times more rigid than paper, but has not proved popular.

Polystyrene (same material as ceiling tiles) reinforced with aluminium foil is very light and rigid and has been used. Its

15

snag is poor damping, it has a characteristic sound which is similar to that heard by tapping a ceiling tile held by one hand at its edge.

Bextrene has been used in many hi-fi speakers being stiffer and more consistent in its characteristics than paper. It too has poor damping and needs to be coated with a plastic damper to tame it. Polypropylene is a more recently employed material and seems to have advantages as a cone material. It is light, has good self-damping, and is more rigid than paper.

So we come back to paper again. If you tap the paper cone of a loudspeaker, all you hear is a dull plop without any readily identifiable sound. This is the ideal for uncoloured reproduction. It is also very light, so the lack of stiffness is the only major snag. But we shall see later, this can be made use of and turned into an advantage.

The paper pulp stock from which loudspeaker cones are made consists of wood and rag with various additives. One stock commonly used is *kapok*, which is produced from the hollow, oily fibres from the silk-cotton tree. These are especially light and strong and so are well suited for this purpose. Waxes, resins and fungicides are added.

Different characteristics can be imparted to the paper pulp stock by the length of the period for which it is beaten out in vats. Long periods produce short fibres which result in thin hard paper. . Cones made from this are light and sensitive, though prone to resonances and poor damping. They are thus more suitable for low-fi transistor radio speakers. Short periods of beating give long fibres, that are more flexible and so less rigid. These are best suited for bass speakers or full-range controlled flexure speakers. It is thus possible to produce a paper for a specific cone application, which is another reason why paper is so popular with the manufacturers.

Cone Resonance
As we have seen, every physical object has a fundamental resonance, that is a frequency at which vibration is greater than at any other for the same input of energy. Loudspeaker cones are no exception, which means that sound output at the resonant frequency is greater than at all others.

16

The result is an uneven frequency response with an unnatural emphasis at that one frequency.

Below the cone resonant frequency, the sound output falls off at a rate of 12 dB per octave, so the frequency response in the bass region is determined to a considerable extent by the resonant frequency which should therefore be as low as possible.

What follows may seem rather technical and can be skipped if desired, but it really is straightforward and involves some fairly elementary maths. If you can get to grips with it, you will understand the behaviour of the loudspeaker cone much better.

The resonant frequency in free air is proportional to the square root of the reciprocal of the mass of the cone times the compliance of the suspension. The formula is:

$$f_r = \frac{1}{2\pi \sqrt{MC}}$$

in which M is the mass in grams and C is the compliance in metres per newton.

Compliance, which is the opposite hence the reciprocal of suspension stiffness, can be calculated from the cone mass and the resonant frequency as follows:

$$C = \frac{1}{(2\pi f_r)^2 \, M}$$

Thus the compliance (the opposite of stiffness) and the mass should be high, but if they are too high other problems can arise. If the suspension is too compliant it may not keep the cone in place at high volume levels; while if the mass is too great, more energy is required to move the cone hence the speaker sensitivity is low and a large amplifier power is needed. The resulting high power dissipation in the coil causes heating with the undesirable effects noted later. Furthermore, as a large mass results in high inertia, the cone will not respond to rapid high frequency electrical signals.

17

Delayed Resonance

In addition to the resonance due to the effect of mass and compliance there is another. When ripples move outward from the centre of the cone to the rim and are not absorbed by the suspension they are reflected back to the centre. When the cone radius equals one wavelength or a multiple of it, the contours of the outward and reflected ripples coincide to produce an apparently stationary ripple or undulation of the cone. It is therefore known as a *standing wave.*

When the electrical signal ceases, the standing wave subsides, and the consequent cone motion radiates sound as it does so. Stored energy is thus released as spurious sound after the signal ceases. The effect is thus termed *delayed resonance.* For an 8-inch cone, the fundamental delayed resonance is at 4 kHz with harmonics at 8 kHz and 16 kHz.

Efficient absorption by the cone surround is vital to minimise the effect for monitor speakers, but the sustained effect thereby produced is often welcomed by lead guitar players.

Another spurious motion performed by some cones at certain frequencies is what is known as the *bell mode.* With this, opposite quadrants of the cone perform a flapping movement in unison, moving backwards and forwards together while the adjacent quadrants flap in the opposite directions. However, two lines at right angles across the cone which define the boundaries of each quadrant remain stationary relative to the flapping. This effect is due to lack of stiffness of the cone itself. Both these effects are considerably reduced in the elliptical loudspeaker.

At the centre of the cone is a dome that serves as a dust shield to prevent foreign particles from getting into the air gap and causing grating noises. At certain high frequencies, this dome sometimes moves independently of the cone, by reason of the compliance of the glued joint. It thereby exhibits its own resonant frequency which colours the reproduction. To avoid this in some models, the dome is moulded as an integral part of the cone.

Some cones have what appears to be a small horn at their centre. This improves the treble response where single units are used to cover the full frequency range.

The Coil

Under the dome at the apex of the cone, lies the coil which consists of a number of turns of copper wire wound on a paper, composition, or aluminium cylinder.

To reduce the mass and thereby the inertia in high frequency speakers, aluminium is sometimes used instead of copper wire. To get as many turns as possible within the magnetic field, the wire is often of square or hexagonal configuration so permitting more turns per inch. Another method is to use ribbon wire wound edgeways on. Up to 40% greater conductor density can thereby be achieved, thus making for a more efficient motor system.

Impedance

Impedance is the total opposition offered to an electric current by the circuit it flows through. It is specified in ohms (Ω). The impedance should match that specified for the amplifier output if maximum transfer of power is to be obtained, but to be avoided at all costs is using a speaker circuit with a lower impedance than that specified for the amplifier. It must be noted that two loudspeakers connected in parallel, across the amplifier, halves their impedance (if they are of the same impedance), while four reduces it to a quarter.

The standard impedance of the coil is 8 ohms, but 4-ohm and 16-ohm models are also available. Formerly, 3 ohms was the standard with 15 ohms for larger units, and these may still be encountered. Two 8-ohm loudspeakers can thus be connected across a 4-ohm output, but no more. Four 8-ohm units would have an impedance of only 2 ohms which would likely burn out a 4-ohm amplifier.

Effects of Heat

The coil is heated by the current flowing through it, and the resistance rises by some 0.4% per degree C. Modern high-power rated speakers have coils wound on aluminium formers secured by high temperature epoxy resin adhesives and can withstand temperatures up to 300°C.

To minimise the effect of heat with high-powered music loudspeakers, various measures are employed to remove it quickly and reduce the temperature build-up. Large magnet

19

assemblies help and sometimes these are blackened and provided with heat fins, but these are long term devices and have little effect on short term temperature variations produced by changing programme content. Treble units being smaller, have a lower maximum temperature than bass drivers, around 120°C. To aid dissipation, some units have gaps between the coil and magnet poles filled with colloidal ferromagnetic fluid held in place by the speaker's magnetic field. This also slightly increases efficiency and provides a measure of damping.

Cone Centring

At the back of the cone, there is a ring of flexible material with corrugations that is secured to the framework at its outer edge and to the cone at its inner. This has the important function of keeping the cone centred relative to the magnet poles. With cheap speakers as used in many transistor radios, the cone can become off-centre due mostly to warping of the thin metal frame so that the magnet poles are not true.

An off-centre cone produces distortion as it rubs against the magnet pole and can be tested for by standing the speaker on its magnet, face upward, and gently pressing the cone inward with the thumbs at opposite points across the diameter, then releasing it. Any rubbing can usually be felt, or heard if an ear is placed close to the cone. Sometimes though, trouble may be experienced from loose coil windings and these may not be detected by this test.

The Magnet

The magnet usually consists of a magnetic ring or rod mounted axially at the back of the speaker. The front pole is terminated by a steel rod pole piece which penetrates inside the coil, and is only slightly of smaller diameter so that the air gap between it and the coil is small. The rear magnet pole is extended by a cylinder or U piece toward the front, where it terminates in a plate with a hole or a ring that surrounds the outside of the coil (Fig.4).

The magnetic field is thus concentrated between the internal rod and the inside of the surrounding hole and thereby through the coil windings. As with all magnets there is a small external leakage field, but modern speakers are designed

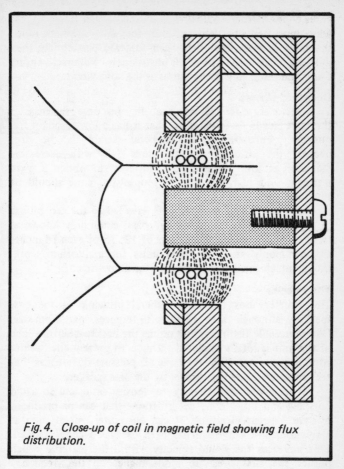

Fig. 4. Close-up of coil in magnetic field showing flux distribution.

to reduce this to a negligible amount. It may seem, when trying to attract a ferrous object with a speaker magnet, that the magnet is weak, but this is the reason. For the same reason there is little possibility of erasing a magnetic tape from the stray field from a modern speaker, this danger is often greatly exaggerated.

Connections from the coil are taken to a couple of soldered blobs on the cone from which highly flexible stranded copper wires connect to a terminal strip on the speaker frame. These wires must never be tight nor must they loop down to touch the cone at any other than their soldered connection; they must be completely free of all obstruction. Failure to ensure this could result in buzzing noises as the cone vibrates.

Dedicated Drivers
To achieve an extended low-frequency response, the mass of the cone needs to be large so that it has a low resonant frequency. Furthermore, its diameter should also be large because the efficiency of the cone falls with decreasing diameter at low frequencies. However, to obtain a good transient and high-frequency response the cone should be small and light.

These conflicting requirements have led to the general use of separate drivers for treble and bass, commonly known as tweeters and woofers. Diameters of 12, 15 or even 18 inches are commonly used for bass units for auditorium work, though much smaller ones are used for domestic hi-fi.

The Tweeter
The tweeter uses the same general principle as the bass speakers, although there are some differences apart from size. One noticeable feature is that unlike the bass speaker the back of the unit is totally enclosed. This is to prevent the tweeter cone being affected by the large air pressure differences that are generated inside the cabinet by the bass speaker.

To achieve a high rigidity to density ratio and so avoid buckling and other cone deformations that can be produced by the high accelerations it can encounter, metal such as aluminium and beryllium has been used as a cone material. This increases the sound velocity within the material which pushes the first break-up mode higher up the frequency scale. However, rigidity can also produce a problem in that there is little or no flexure, so the radiation resistance falls off at an earlier point than with a less rigid cone and the treble response suffers accordingly. The use of metal-coned tweeters thus tends to be confined to narrow bandwidths, with super-tweeters covering the highest octave or so. Other than these, paper with a high kapok content and mica are the principal materials.

Another feature with many tweeters is that the conventional cone is reversed to form a dome. This overcomes some of the problems associated with cones and gives a wider angle of dispersion. High frequencies generated by a cone form a narrow beam so that those sitting off axis get very little, while those in line often get too much. A dome tends to disperse high frequencies and reduce beaming. Some models have acoustic lenses which perform a similar function.

To achieve a higher sound output some tweeters are equipped with a horn in front of the cone. These permit a more effective coupling between cone and air, the principle being more fully discussed in a later chapter.

As mentioned earlier, temperature rise can be a problem as the small size does not lend itself to rapid dissipation of heat. Liquid cooling of the air gap with colloidal ferromagnetic fluid which also helps to concentrate the magnetic flux is employed with some models.

It is necessary to split the signal into two, one containing all the high frequencies and the other the low, by a filter circuit termed a *crossover network*, and fed to the respective drivers. Bass fed to a tweeter would rapidly destroy it.

The large woofers used for stage work not only are unable to reproduce high treble but also very little in the mid-range. Tweeters cannot handle down into the middle frequencies at high power, so a mid-frequency range speaker is also commonly used for full-range keyboard or monitor work. With domestic systems the bass unit can go higher and the tweeter lower, so mid-range units are less common.

Controlled Flexure

There are many disadvantages in using separate bass, mid and treble units. They do not cut off abruptly but gradually so that both drivers are working together at frequencies around the crossover point. When all units are in the same cabinet, they can mutually interfere with each other with the sound from the one actually cancelling that from the other in certain circumstances. There are also distortions caused by the crossover circuit, and difficulties in maintaining balance over the whole frequency and power range.

So there is much to be said for the use of a single unit to cover the whole range if high fidelity is desired. Yet in theory as we have seen, a single speaker cannot cover a wide frequency range, but in practice they actually do. How then do they manage it?

The answer lies in the flexure of the cone at different frequencies. At high frequencies, the central area of the cone responds, but the rest of the cone remains stationary because of its inertia. This independent movement of the central area is possible because of flexure of the non-rigid cone around that area. As the frequency decreases, so larger areas of the cone are brought into play, until at low frequencies the whole cone is in motion (Fig.5).

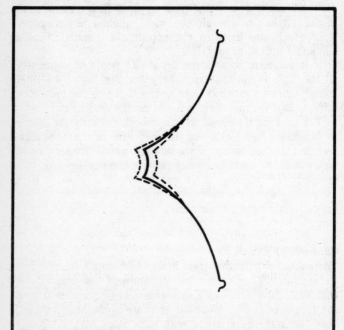

Fig.5. Controlled flexure. At high frequencies the central areas of a curved cone move independently of the rest. The higher the frequency the smaller the active area. This thus serves as an effective high frequency radiator.

24

This effect occurs to some extent with most loudspeakers, but some cones are specially made to exploit it. These have curved sides, and the flexure points are designed into them so that a smooth coverage of a wide frequency range is achieved. They often have a small horn fixed to the centre of the cone to increase efficiency at high frequencies.

Although not having quite the range of separate drivers, it is by no means inadequate, a typical specification being 40 Hz to 17 kHz. Such full-range drivers as they are called, avoid all the problems of having multiple drivers, and have few vices. They have thus much to commend them for hi-fi use. For high power musical instrument loudspeakers the large bass units are not made to reproduce treble in this manner, and so multiple units are unavoidable for full-range applications. They can be used though for lower-power fill-ins and monitors.

Cone Velocity and Radiation Resistance

The effect of cone inertia is to limit its acceleration, just as a heavy lorry which has considerable inertia, cannot get away so quickly from the lights as the motor bike. As the frequency rises and the cone makes more excursions per second its speed needs to increase to maintain the same amplitude. This requires more power, but if the power is constant the speed must also be constant. So when the frequency rises, the amplitude of the cone excursions must decrease to maintain the same speed.

This means that the sound volume diminishes as the frequency increases, an effect which without compensation would give a very poor treble reproduction.

Fortuitously, and by one of those rare quirks of the laws of physics, there is another defect in the way sound is propagated by a loudspeaker cone that almost exactly cancels the effect of the first. This is *radiation resistance*. At low frequencies the cone is an inefficient sound radiator. It pushes the air out of the way instead of compressing it.

As the frequency increases, the air does not move aside fast enough to avoid compression but offers a resistance to the cone and so produces sound. The higher the frequency up to a certain point, the greater the radiation resistance and the more efficient the air coupling to the cone. Thus the acoustic output rises and exactly compensates for the diminishing cone excursions.

The compensating effect works up to a point when the radiation resistance is at a maximum and cannot increase further. This frequency range is termed the *piston region* of operation. Above this the response begins to fall off because the cone excursions due to velocity effect continue to decrease. However, cone flexure effects maintain the response further, and also the beaming effect at high frequencies increasingly concentrate the sound in front of the cone. Thus a useful response continues well above the piston region so making full-range single-unit speakers viable.

The piston region transition point is dependent on the diameter of the cone. For a flat radiator in a true infinite baffle, the relation between the transition frequency and the cone diameter is:

$$f = \frac{68,275}{\pi d}$$

in which d is the cone diameter in centimetres.

It can thus be seen that though simple in principle, there is a lot more to the moving-coil loudspeaker driver than may at first appear.

Chapter 3

BEING BAFFLED

When the cone of a moving coil speaker moves backwards and forwards it generates two separate sound waves, one at the front and the other at the back. Air is compressed in one direction while that in the other is rarefied. The two waves are thus said to be out of phase.

Phase differences are often present when two or more loudspeakers operate in close proximity as they often do in stage stacks. If one speaker should be connected the opposite way to an adjacent one that is connected to the same amplifier, its cone will be travelling backward while the other is going forward, so one produces a compression while the other generates an expansion wave. Where the waves meet there is mutual interference and cancellation, resulting in zero or a very low sound level.

Cancellation also occurs when the front and rear waves meet at the rim of the loudspeaker. Radiated sound then consists only of high frequencies having a wavelength shorter than the radius of the cone, as one or more complete cycles of these are propagated before cancellation occurs at the rim. This accounts for the familiar tinny effect when a loudspeaker is operated without a baffle.

The Baffle

It is evident then that some means must be provided to keep the two out-of-phase waves physically apart, and an obvious way to do so is to mount the speaker on a large flat board termed a baffle. They still meet at the edge, but they have further to go and so longer wavelengths can be propagated before cancellation takes place. Thus the bass response is extended compared to that of an unmounted speaker (Fig.6). The straightforward baffle has many advantages, among which is the lack of air resonance that produces the colouration inherent with an enclosure. Also panel resonances and vibrations common with cabinets are minimal.

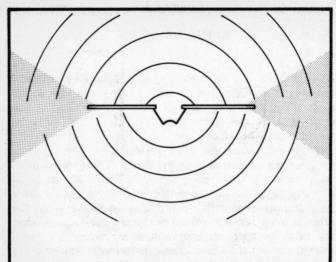

Fig.6. Flat baffle. Extends front/back path via which out-of-phase sound waves merge and cancel, thus lowering the frequency at which cancellation occurs.

One potential snag is that because of the time taken for the rear sound waves to reach the edge of the baffle, delays occur which at some frequencies can mean that a compression wave from the rear is propagated at the same time as the next compression wave from the front, so that they actually reinforce each other. At other frequencies the opposite occurs and cancellation takes place.

Reinforcement occurs at wavelengths that are 0.5, 1.5, 2.5 . . . times the radius of the baffle, whereas cancellation takes place at whole multiples, 1.0, 2.0, 3.0 . . . times the radius. The effect is a very uneven frequency response with alternate peaks and troughs throughout its range.

It can be easily avoided though by simply mounting the speaker off centre on the baffle. There is thus no uniform radius and the cancellation and reinforcement effects are smoothed out. A rectangular baffle with the speaker off centre gives good results, but a circular or square one with the speaker at the centre is the worst possible case (Fig.7).

Fig.7. *A speaker in the centre of a square baffle has an almost equal radius to the baffle edge so cancellation occurs at whole multiples of the radius wavelength and reinforcement at half multiples. This effect is avoided in a rectangular baffle where the radius is not the same in all directions thus smoothing out interference effects.*

The big problem with an open baffle lies in the size of baffle needed to procure an adequate bass response. To achieve a flat response down to 45 Hz, requires a baffle with the shortest radius of 25 ft (7.7 m). That means a width and height of more than 50 ft, which is obviously impractical.

Looking at more practical dimensions, a 2 ft radius which is a 4 ft width or height would be about the maximum. This would start to roll off at 280 Hz which is rather high, but an ameliorating factor is that the bass fall-off is only 6 dB per octave. This means a —6 dB response at 140 Hz, and a —12 dB level at 70 Hz. The bass response of most enclosures drops sharply below their rated limit, so with a baffle of this size there is at least some response in the bass though not very much. While an extended bass response is unnecessary for speech, and in fact can be detrimental to clarity, it is essential for music, especially live music on stage, so the open baffle is a non-starter.

Adding Sides

The dimensions of a baffle can be practically increased by adding sides, a top and a bottom. The front-to-back path is thereby extended, slightly improving the bass response.

A further step is to add a back in which a number of slots have been cut. This adds to the front-to-back path and the slots serve as an acoustic resistance to the rear wave. So the bass is noticeably increased. However, the enclosed air space has a more pronounced resonance which affects the reproduction. Alternatively, the back can be solid thus blocking off the rear wave completely. For this reason the enclosure is often called an infinite baffle.

A pronounced air resonance in the bass can result unless the size of the enclosure is carefully designed to match the particular driver being used. But more of this in the next chapter.

Chapter 4

THE INFINITE BAFFLE

In the last chapter we saw that the cabinet is not just a convenient means of mounting the loudspeaker driver but serves the essential purpose of keeping the out-of-phase waves generated by the front and the rear of the loudspeaker cone apart. One of the most common methods of doing this is by simply sealing up the back of the cabinet so that the rear wave is trapped and cannot escape. We will take a look at this method more closely. Like the loudspeaker itself, although simple in concept there is a lot to be considered in the actual design.

The bass driver used for this type of enclosure requires a weaker or more compliant suspension than other types because the springiness of the trapped air restrains the cone movement and therefore itself serves as a suspension. The driver and the enclosure is therefore often described as of the *acoustic suspension* type.

An important restriction must be observed with these drivers. They should never be used in ordinary unsealed cabinets at frequencies below the point at which the bass response of the cabinet begins to roll off. Without the cushion of air behind the cone, the mechanical suspension is too weak to hold it in place by itself, and damage would soon result.

The big snag with this principle is that the air cushion can considerably modify the motion of the cone, and so distort the front sound wave radiated from it. The resonant frequency of a bass driver in a sealed box should be as low as possible, because the response falls off rapidly at the rate of 12 dB per octave below it.

The damping effect of the trapped air on the cone decreases compliance and results in a raising of its resonant frequency. The larger the box, the greater the volume of air it encloses, the larger its compliance and the smaller its dampening effect. This is so because a given cone excursion exercises less compression on a large air volume than on a small volume. So for infinite baffle enclosures with a given driver, *a large box has a lower resonant frequency than a small one.*

Using the same logic, a small cone compresses a given air volume less than a large cone. So the cone size also influences the enclosure resonant frequency, hence *a small cone produces a lower enclosure resonant frequency than a large one.* However, because of its smaller mass it had a higher free-air resonance to start with.

Putting all this together, three things affect the resonant frequency of the enclosure: (1) air volume, hence box size; (2) cone size; and (3) cone mass. As we have seen, the compliance of the cone surround also affects the resonant frequency, but with this type of driver the surround compliance is a minor factor compared to that of the air in the box.

A desired resonant frequency can thus be obtained by selection of these three factors. If one or two are immutable, then the required result can be achieved by selecting the other. The accompanying chart shows the relationships and enables a selection to be made (Fig.8).

Damping and Q
At the enclosure resonant frequency, the cone excursion is larger than at all other frequencies, hence the sound output is greater, and a peak appears in the frequency response. If undamped, this results in a boomy sounding bass, one note predominates, in fact the effect has been dubbed 'one-note bass'.

The magnification of cone movement at resonance compared to that at other frequencies is denoted by the letter Q. Students of electronics will recognise that this is the term applied to an inductor to denote its reactance divided by its resistance. A high Q means the coil will tune sharply with a large peak and so it is rated as a quality factor, hence the designation. In the case of a loudspeaker, the same term is used to describe a like magnification at a resonant frequency.

When a loudspeaker cone is impelled backwards and forwards by the applied electrical signal, the coil windings cut through the magnetic field so generating a voltage in them. This is of opposite polarity to the applied voltage, hence it is

32

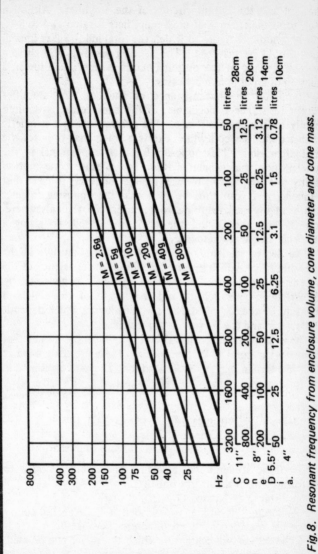

Fig.8. Resonant frequency from enclosure volume, cone diameter and cone mass.

33

termed *back emf*. It produces a current which flows through the coil and the output circuits of the amplifier. Although the output impedance of most amplifiers is rated at 4 to 8 Ω, this is a nominal figure to which the total loudspeaker impedance should be matched. The actual resistance offered to a current flowing in the output circuits is very much lower, a fraction of an ohm in most cases.

Compared to the resistance of the coil, the amplifier output resistance is negligible, so the back current is limited mainly by the coil resistance. The current sets up a magnetic field around the coil which exerts a force that opposes the original motion. This opposing force is proportional to the cone motion that generated it, so an excessive cone motion at any one frequency produces a larger opposing force at that frequency. It can thus be seen that the opposing force is greater at any peak resulting from a resonance, than elsewhere, and thereby the Q and the peak is reduced, so giving a smoother frequency response.

The degree of damping depends on the magnitude of the opposing force, which in turn depends on the efficiency of the system as a generator. Generator efficiency is governed by the magnetic flux density and the length of the coil, and inversely by the coil resistance, the cone inertia which depends on its mass, and the frequency of resonance.

There are thus mechanical factors and electrical ones that make up the total Q of the system. These are designated as Q_{ms} and Q_{es} in maker's specifications. They are combined in the following formula to describe the total Q of a driver, Q_{ts}:

$$Q_{ts} = \frac{Q_{ms} \times Q_{es}}{Q_{ms} + Q_{es}} \quad \text{or} \quad \frac{1}{Q_{ts}} = \frac{1}{Q_{ms}} + \frac{1}{Q_{es}}$$

Electronic students will recognise this as being similar to the formula for resistors in parallel.

The total Q designated Q_{ts}, is that of the driver only. The total including the cabinet is described as Q_{tc}. This of course cannot be specified by a manufacturer because he does not know the size of the cabinet in which the driver will be used, but it does appear in formula which we can use to determine the optimum cabinet size as we shall see.

These descriptions incidentally, along with a number of others, are what are known as the *Thiele-Small* parameters after the two researchers Neville Thiele and Richard Small who mathematically related and documented the various factors governing loudspeaker behaviour in the early 1970s.

If Q_{tc} is equal to unity, there is no peak at the resonant frequency because the amplitude of the cone excursion is just 1 times that at any other frequency. This would appear to be the ideal value. However, an undamped response consists of a peak that is sharp at its tip while being fairly broad at its base. If now we level the tip to unity value, there is still a slight rise on either side due to the 'foothills' of the base. The lower one disappears due to the bass roll-off below resonance, but the upper one remains.

A Q_{tc} of unity therefore produces a small rise just above the resonant frequency. The chart shows the effect (Fig.9). To eliminate this, we need a Q_{tc} that is actually less than unity. This is possible by reducing the cone diameter, or for a given driver, increasing the volume of air in the enclosure, which means increasing its size.

The optimum value to obtain a smooth response is 0.7, although this causes a bass roll-off slightly higher than the resonant frequency. If the resonant frequency can be made low by having a large enclosure, the small sacrifice in bass is worth it in order to get a smooth and more natural response. With small enclosures a Q_{tc} of unity may be necessary to extend the bass as far as possible which means to the resonant frequency. The slight rise just above it further emphasizes the bass and gives the impression of a good bass response, although it is at the expense of naturalness and will give a somewhat boomy result.

Enclosure Size

The formula for designing a sealed enclosure for a particular driver is quite a complex one, but it can be greatly simplified if its use is restricted to a Q_{tc} of 0.7. For other values it is less accurate. The governing factors are: the compliance of the drive unit's suspension; the volume of air having the same compliance; the mechanical Q, Q_{ms}; and the electrical Q, Q_{es}.

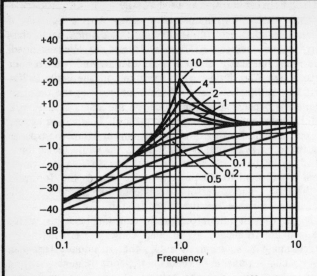

Fig.9. Response at resonant frequency for different values of Q.

To simplify matters further, these four factors are combined into two in the Thiele-Small parameters quoted in maker's specifications. The volume of a body of air having the same compliance as the suspension of the drive unit is given in litres and denoted by the term V_{as}. The mechanical and electrical Q are usually combined according to the previous formula and given as Q_{ts}.

So we need only the V_{as} and the Q_{ts}. The formula is:

$$V_b = \frac{V_{as} \times Q_{ts}^2}{Q_{tc}^2 - Q_{ts}^2} \quad \text{as } Q_{tc} \text{ is } 0.7,$$

then
$$V_b = \frac{V_{as} \times Q_{ts}^2}{0.49 - Q_{ts}^2}$$

Not all bass drivers have the high compliance required for use in sealed enclosures, many are designed for open-backed systems. If this formula is used for these, it will produce a cabinet volume of impractical size.

The volume V_b is of air in litres, so it is the internal dimensions that we must use for calculation, and any major internal solids must be deducted. The principal one would be the bass driver itself. The volume of this can be approximately calculated by regarding it as a cone. To find the volume of a cone we multiply the area of the base (the speaker cone) by the height (distance from the front of the unit to the back of the magnet) and divide the result by three. Area of the base is given by πr^2. So:

$$V = \frac{\pi r^2 h}{3}$$

in which V is the volume, r is the cone radius, and h is the height.

Approximate values for different loudspeaker diameters are: 10-inch, 1.5 litres; 12-inch, 3 litres; 15-inch, 6 litres; 18-inch, 12 litres.

If you are working in inches, multiply the width, height and depth of the inside of the proposed cabinet, divide by 61 and you will have the total volume in litres. Deduct the amount for the bass driver to give the net volume. Adjust any measurement and re-calculate until you get the figure calculated for the specific driver. If working in millimetres multiply the three measurements and divide by 1,000,000 to give the volume.

The bass response can be worked out from the resonant frequency of the driver in free air f_s. It is defined as the frequency at which the output has fallen by 3 dB, indicated as f_3. For a sealed enclosure the response drops below that at about the rate of 12 dB per octave. For a Q_{tc} of 0.7 the formula for the f_3 point is:

$$f_3 = \frac{0.7 \, f_s}{Q_{ts}}$$

Increasing the size of a sealed box with a specific driver does not increase the bass response. It only lowers the Q_{tc} which changes the shape of the response giving a gentler slope with less distortion, but which may actually give the impression of less bass. Using the f_3 level as a reference, the chart on page 39 depicts six typical loudspeakers showing the f_3 of each with the Q_{tc} plotted against the cabinet volume in litres. The optimum value nearest a Q_{tc} of 0.7 is emboldened.

Sensitivity

The amount of acoustic output from a given electric input is what is meant by the term sensitivity, not the way the speaker responds to transient or other types of signal unless that is specifically stated. For the infinite baffle speaker the sensitivity is low. The reason is not hard to understand. In order to achieve a low resonant frequency and thereby obtain an extended bass response without a very large enclosure, the mass of the bass driver is made large. Mass requires power to move it, so more power is needed to do so than for a driver with a lighter cone.

Efficiency, hence sensitivity could be increased by making the magnet stronger, but this reduces the Q and results in overdamping. In turn, overdamping eliminates the effect of resonance on the bass response and results in the bass roll-off starting at a much higher frequency. The rather unexpected result is that many small speakers need a higher amplifier power than larger ones, simply because they are made less efficient in order to get a better bass response.

Dimensional Resonances

In addition to the main air/cone resonance we have here discussed, there are air resonances that are functions of the three enclosure dimensions. These resonances occur when the dimension is equal to half a wavelength, and if undamped will cause colouration of the reproduced sound at the corresponding frequencies.

The first thing to ensure is that none of the dimensions is the same. Height, width and depth must all be different. This applies also to multiples of those dimensions so that one should not be a half, third or a quarter the size of another. To

Cone diameter	12-inch		12-inch		12-inch		15-inch		15-inch		18-inch	
V_b litres	f_3	Q	f_3	Q	f_3	Q	f_3	Q	f_3	Q	f_3	Q
40	89	.89	92	.85								
50	86	.79	90	.75	75	.79						
60	**85**	**.73**	**89**	**.69**	74	.73						
70	85	.65	90	.65	**74**	**.69**						
80	86	.64	91	.61	75	.65	68	.80				
90					75	.63	67	.76	85	.78		
100							67	.73	84	.74		
110							**67**	**.70**	84	**.71**	56	.80
120							67	.68	**84**	.69	55	.77
130							67	.66	84	.67	55	.74
140							68	.65	84	.66	**55**	**.72**
150									85		55	.69
160											55	.67

avoid similar problems in listening rooms, what is known as the *golden ratio* is often invoked. This is to make the dimensions of the room comply with the ratio 1 : 1.6 : 2.5. Any of these can be multiples or sub-multiples such as 1 : 3.2 : 2.5.

The same rule can be applied to infinite baffle enclosures in order to spread the resonances and avoid any coinciding. Should this happen, there would be a very pronounced peak at the frequency corresponding to the half-wavelength. Even worse would be a square box or a rectangle having the same width and depth with the height double the width. That would cause a very strong resonance and severe colouration.

As with the unsealed cabinet, an irregular shape with non-parallel sides reduces dimensional resonance effects. The ultimate shape for doing this is a pyramid, and at least one commercial speaker has been made in this form. The disadvantage apart from the woodworking problems, is that a pyramid has only a third of the volume of a rectangle of the same base area and height. So, either the base and/or height must be increased to compensate, or the reduced bass response must be accepted. As speakers are expected to be compact and have a good bass response, it can be appreciated why the pyramid has not caught on commercially.

When a resonance is excited between two parallel surfaces such as the sides, top and bottom or front and back of an enclosure, what are called *standing waves* are set up. As the half cycles of the waves travelling back and forth are exactly the same length as the space between the surfaces, the respective areas of high and low compression always appear in the same place and so the wave seems to be standing still. The points of minimum vibration are termed the *nodes*, while those of maximum motion are called the *antinodes*.

At the fundamental resonance frequency the antinodes appear half-way between the surfaces, which is at the middle of the enclosure. However, each frequency is accompanied by a number of harmonics, that is further frequencies at double, treble, four times, etc., the frequency of the fundamental. These also have a pattern of nodes and antinodes.

The second harmonic has antinodes at one-third and two-thirds of the dimension; the third harmonic antinodes are at one-sixth, a half and five-sixths the length. Antinodes of the fourth harmonic appear at one-eighth, three-eighths, five-eighths and seven-eighths, and so on.

Dimensional resonances can be damped by the placing of absorbent material at the antinode positions where the vibrational motion is greatest. It has virtually no effect at the nodes. From the above it is evident that the nodes of the fundamental and all the harmonics are at the surfaces themselves, so material fixed to the cabinet walls have no effect on these resonances. As there are many antinodes of the fundamental and the harmonics spaced across the dimension, and there are further ones from the other two dimensions in the same space, it follows that to be effective, damping material should fill the whole enclosure.

This is done in most of the small enclosures with thick rolled-up layers occupying most of the space. The material used is of a cellular form, so air is present throughout, but the passage of sound pressure waves is impeded. The presence of this material also slightly increases the effective volume of the enclosure because of its slowing down effect on the sound waves passing through it. They thus take longer to reach the boundary wall just as if the dimension was longer and the wall was further away.

With large enclosures such as those used for public performances with musical instruments there are practical difficulties in completely filling the volume with absorbent. The problem is that the weight causes the material to compact at the bottom and leave gaps at the top. It should not be compressed too much as this forces out the air and so effectively reduces the internal air volume of the enclosure. One solution to this is to fix several 'shelves' of nylon netting (not wire which could vibrate) across the cabinet to support the layers of absorbent. However, large cabinets for use with musical instruments are rarely totally filled because of this problem of compaction and the large quantities that would be required.

Panel Resonance
There is yet a further type of resonance which can colour the reproduction from a sealed box type of speaker. The fact that the box *is* sealed and no air can escape produces large pressure

41

differences between the inside surfaces and the external ones which are at the normal atmospheric pressure.

These differences cause the walls of the enclosure to vibrate in and out in sympathy with the pressure differences. They thus produce sound, but because they also have particular resonant frequencies and their motion is not in linear proportion to the pressure, the sound they radiate is highly coloured.

So it is necessary to reduce panel vibrations to the minimum and many different materials and types of construction have been tried with this end in view. One of the best is brick or concrete which has a high density and so a high resistance to lateral vibration. The practical problems are fairly obvious, as concrete enclosures could hardly be called transportable.

A very effective alternative is sand-filled panels. Each panel is constructed of two sheets of wood separated by square-section moulding around three edges, then sand is poured into the space between them. The fourth edge is finally sealed with a length of moulding. The panels must be made to the correct size as they obviously cannot be cut afterward (Fig.10). Weight is considerable, which rather eliminates it for travelling instrumental use, the weight of the drivers in large enclosures is heavy enough as it is!

Perhaps the most common material used is ½- or ¾-inch plywood, but it is very prone to vibrate without bracing or damping. To improve matters, many designs employ cross-bracing to improve rigidity. While it does this to a certain extent it is not all that effective in reducing vibrations.

The trick is to fit the bracing at the points where the maximum amplitude of vibration occurs, the antinodes. One way of doing this experimentally requires the use of an audio oscillator. The cabinet with drivers in place is temporarily sealed with its back and laid so that the panel under test is uppermost. An amplifier is connected and the oscillator output applied to its input.

Powdered chalk is scattered evenly over the panel, and the amplifier turned well up. The frequency of the oscillator is varied over the low to mid frequency range until the chalk settles in a discernible pattern. The regions where there is no chalk are those of maximum vibration and are the ones that need bracing. If an oscillator is not available, the same

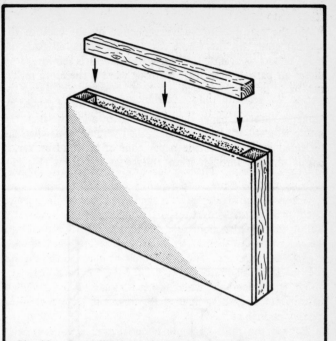

Fig. 10. Sand-filled panel. Two wooden sheets are assembled with square-section along three sides. The cavity is filled with sand and the fourth square-section fitted. Seal all joints to prevent sand leakage.

result could be obtained by using a synthesizer or electronic organ. Slowly play an ascending scale including semitones from the lowest note up to middle C and watch the chalk pattern take shape.

Struts and battens reinforce one point only whereas the vibration nearly always occurs over a larger area. A better method is to use a partition along the affected region. It should have plenty of large holes drilled in it to allow the free passage of sound pressure waves through.

Reflected Wave

While the rear pressure wave generated by the back of the speaker cone fills the whole enclosure affecting all parts, its main impact is against the rear wall where it is reinforced by direct air particle velocity. A strong wave is therefore reflected back to the loudspeaker. Now paper is transparent to sound waves of mid and lower frequencies as can be proved by taping a sheet of paper over the front of a loudspeaker, the sound is heard at almost undiminished volume. So, when the reflected wave reaches the paper cone of the loudspeaker, it passes straight through it to emerge at the front (Fig.11).

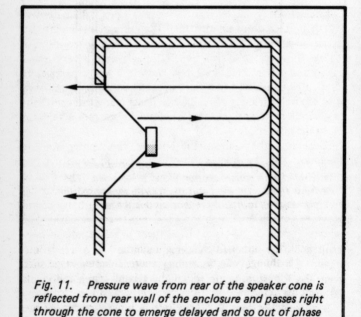

Fig. 11.   Pressure wave from rear of the speaker cone is reflected from rear wall of the enclosure and passes right through the cone to emerge delayed and so out of phase with the original.

However, it is delayed compared to the original, by the amount of time it took to travel to and from the rear enclosure wall. When the depth of the enclosure is equal to a quarter or three-quarters of a wavelength, the reflected wave reinforces the original, but when the dimension is a half or a whole wavelength or a multiple, the wave cancels it. Thus we get a series of peaks and troughs in the frequency response corresponding to those frequencies that are reinforced and cancelled.

Sometimes an audible 'honk' is produced by the interaction of the reflected wave with the next cone excursion. To reduce the reflected wave to a minimum, the rear wall must be heavily damped with absorbents or damping pads, it being of greater importance here than anywhere else.

Considerations

It can be seen from all this then that producing an infinite baffle speaker is by no means a case of simply mounting a driver or two in a sealed box, although that is how some speaker manufacturers appear to view it. Many parameters have to be considered in order to get the design right and even then reputable makers often have to make many trial-and-error modifications to the prototype before the speaker is released on to the market.

Generally, the smaller the speaker the tighter are the tolerances and the greater the effect of small errors. A real problem is the choice of either an apparently extended bass or a smooth bass. The difficulties in subduing the dimensional and panel resonances inherent with sealing up a hefty sound pressure wave in an airtight box also must be met; rather like sealing a genie in a bottle! If all these problems are successfully tackled, good results can be obtained.

There is though one remaining inherent disadvantage with the airtight enclosure for which there is no real solution. It can best be understood by comparison with a bicycle pump. If you slide the extended handle of a bicycle pump inward with the exit hole free, what little resistance it meets is the same along its whole travel. If now you do the same with a finger pressed over the exit hole, the resistance though slight to start with gets progressively greater until it is virtually impossible to push the handle the last few inches. The reason is because the internal air pressure increases with the inward travel of the handle.

A similar principle applies to a loudspeaker cone working against the air in a sealed box; there is little resistance to the initial cone movement, but as the cone travels further inward, the internal pressure rises and offers an increasing back pressure. According to Newton's Laws of Motion, the movement of a body is the result of *all* the forces acting upon it. So, the cone excursion is progressively reduced the further it travels; its motion is not solely dependant on the applied signal as it is when on an open baffle. A similar effect exists when the cone moves outward, it creates an increasing vacuum as it does, so its outward excursion is likewise inhibited (Fig.12).

The result is a non-linear response to the applied signal. However, at mid and high frequencies the cone has completed its excursion and is moving in the opposite direction before the pressure has had time to build up and exert a back force. So at these frequencies, there is little audible effect, but at the lower ones in the bass register, non-linear back pressure causes high harmonic distortion. The larger the cabinet the lower the frequency at which non-linear back pressure starts having an effect, so small cabinets suffer the most.

Overall then, the sealed box speaker can produce deeper bass than any other of similar size, but at best the bass will have high harmonic distortion, and at worst will have boom and sundry other colorations along with it. Such coloration, though a disadvantage for hi-fi, is not such a drawback for musical instrument loudspeakers in which it can add timbre and character to the sound and this type of enclosure is extensively used.

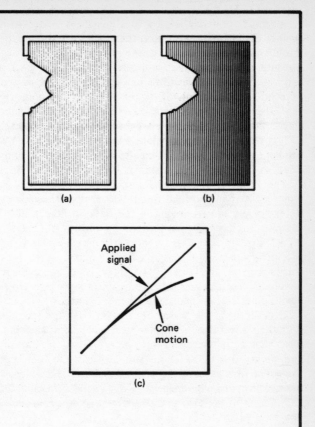

(a)　　　　　　　(b)

Applied
signal

Cone
motion

(c)

Fig. 12.　When the cone moves inward in a sealed
enclosure (a) pressure increases (b) exerting an opposing
force in the cone. It thus does not follow the applied
signal at the extremities of cone excursion (c), adding
distortion. The effect occurs only at low frequencies.

47

Chapter 5

THE REFLEX ENCLOSURE

The reflex enclosure is airtight like the infinite baffle, except for a small vent or *port* at the front through which some of the rear sound can escape. Usually, the port has a small inlet pipe penetrating into the enclosure. The basic principle behind this is that at low frequencies the rear wave is delayed and so emerges later in phase with the front wave, thereby reinforcing it (Fig.13).

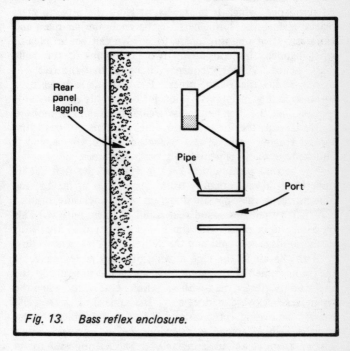

Fig. 13.   Bass reflex enclosure.

The air in the inlet pipe is isolated from the rest of the air in the enclosure except at its inside end. It has mass and inertia and so has a resonant frequency of its own which is largely independent of that in the enclosure. The pipe is so proportioned that its resonant frequency is the same as that of the cone and enclosure air combined. Having two resonances at the same frequency may seem disastrous in view of what has been said about similar cabinet resonances. However, it is the way in which the air masses react with each other that gives the desired effect.

At high frequencies the inertia of the air in the pipe is too great for it to respond so at these, the enclosure behaves as if it were a totally sealed cabinet, and performance is similar to an infinite baffle.

Interaction at Resonance

At resonance, which is in the bass region, the pipe air mass reacts against the springiness of the enclosure air mass and vibrates but in opposite phase to it. We can get an idea of what happens by considering two pendulums of the same mass, hence swinging frequency, hung so that the free end of one strikes that of the other. The first one is driven by a force so that it maintains a constant backwards and forwards motion. At the first strike, the second pendulum is knocked outward and the first reverses then returns to meet the second coming back. There is another strike, the second is knocked outward again and the process continues.

The second pendulum is kept moving by the first but its direction is always opposite to it. So too the air mass in the pipe moves in the opposite direction to the enclosure air mass and thereby radiates sound that is out of phase with it. This of course is in phase with the sound generated by the front of the loudspeaker cone and the desired reinforcement occurs.

With the air in the pipe moving outward at resonance at the same time as the cone, the decompression inside the enclosure is greater than with an infinite baffle, and when the air moves backward it does so at the same time as the cone thereby increasing compression. Thus the movement of the cone is highly damped at resonance and its excursion is no greater than at other frequencies. This is opposite to its normal behaviour by which cone excursion is greater at resonance. It can thus handle a larger signal without driving it beyond the limits at which non-linear distortion and straining of the suspension can occur. Its power handling capacity is thereby increased.

Returning to our analogy of the pendulums, if we visualize them as being linked at their free ends with elastic or a spring, we can get a more accurate idea of what happens especially at higher frequencies. The first pendulum is made to swing much faster so that the second when struck hardly has time to move before it is being pulled back by the elastic, and when it begins to respond to this pull it is struck again. So it really doesn't know whether it is coming or going and its inertia prevents it from hardly moving at all. This is just the situation at high frequencies we described for the two air masses which are linked by their mutual elasticity. The higher the frequency the less the response of the second air mass will be.

Let us now imagine though that the first pendulum is slowed right down. It meets the second one but instead of knocking it on it gently pushes it forward, and when it reverses, the second one does also. So, the second pendulum moves under the influence of the first as before, but this time it travels in the same direction, they move together.

This is what happens to the air mass in the pipe at frequencies below resonance. It has insufficient inertia to bounce back and it follows the same movement and direction as that of the enclosure air mass. So it behaves as a simple leak in the baffle and the rear wave emerges out-of-phase to cancel the wave from the front.

Disadvantages

The cancellation effects below resonance produce a very sharp drop in output, up to 24 dB per octave. This is partly due to the high efficiency above resonance which is around 5 dB or three times the output of an infinite baffle enclosure. The fall from this must therefore be more rapid. While the high efficiency is desirable, a rapid drop can result in 'ringing' and other unmusical effects in the bass register. A gentler slope gives better subjective results even if it starts at a higher frequency and thereby curtails the bass somewhat.

Another snag is that only the minimum amount of lagging can be used inside the enclosure because lagging reduces Q, and as the enclosure air resonance plays such an important part in the operation, a high Q is essential. Thus panel resonances and other problems resulting from insufficient lagging may be encountered. The back panel should be lagged though to prevent a reflected wave passing out through the loudspeaker cone.

As all resonant objects store energy then subsequently release it, this happens also with the reflex enclosure. Sound is thereby radiated after the cessation of the input signal. This gives rise to a rather muddled effect especially on bass transients such as string bass pizzicato notes.

A further drawback with the reflex enclosure is that air turbulence is generated around the pipe and vent which can produce noise at high volume levels, although this can be minimised by having a large vent area. With smaller enclosures friction losses around the vent can reduce the advantage of high efficiency.

Auxiliary Bass Radiator

As an alternative to the pipe, a device similar to a dummy loudspeaker is sometimes used. It is a cone and suspension without the magnet and coil, its mass serving as a substitute for that of the air in the pipe. It avoids the pipe noise and air turbulence and also serves as a barrier to mid-frequencies which may radiate through a vent from internal reflections. Its mass can be precisely designed for a specific enclosure, and it can be made to resonate at the required frequency in a smaller enclosure than would be possible with a normal vent.

Impedance

With an infinite baffle enclosure, the cone excursions are larger at resonance than at any other frequency, although the acoustic output may not be greater because of the damping introduced by a Q that is less than unity. The back emf which is generated by the coil transversing the magnetic field, is therefore also greater at resonance, as is the opposing current it produces.

Thus the total forward current (signal current minus back current) is smaller. The effective impedance of the circuit is therefore greater. A graph of the impedance of any loudspeaker in an infinite baffle enclosure will show a peak at the

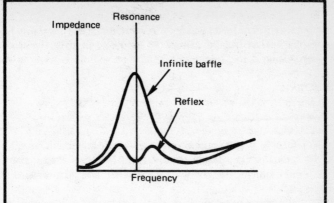

Fig. 14. Impedance chart comparing infinite baffle with reflex enclosure.

resonant frequency. In fact if such a graph is published with the speaker specification, one can determine the resonant frequency from it more easily than from the frequency response chart.

In the case of the reflex enclosure, the cone is physically restrained by the air loading as we have seen, so its excursion is less than it is at the surrounding frequencies. Back emf and current is thereby reduced so instead of a peak there is a dip in the impedance at resonance. However, on approaching resonance from either side, the cone starts a more vigorous motion, but it dies down at the actual resonant frequency. Thus are obtained two small impedance peaks equally spaced either side of resonance. These clearly identify a reflex speaker (Fig.14).

They appear as such only when the two resonant systems are at the same frequency which is when the reflex action is working properly. With small enclosures, some designers tune the tube air mass to a slightly higher frequency than that of the enclosure, and this shows up as a pair of unequal peaks, the lower being the largest.

Enclosure Design

Construction must be sturdy of a dense material to avoid panel resonances as lagging cannot be used except over the back. The formula for calculating enclosure volume is as follows:

$$V = \pi r^2 \frac{4.66 \ 10^6}{f^2 (L + 1.7r)} + L \ \text{ins}^2$$

in which V is the volume of the enclosure in cubic inches; r is the radius of the speaker cone; L is the length of the tube; and f is the resonant frequency of the speaker; all measurements in inches.

If you prefer to work in metric units the following is an approximate equivalent, all measurements in cm.

$$V = \pi r^2 \frac{304 \ 10^6}{f^2 (L + 1.7r)} + L \ \text{cm}^2 \ .$$

For this formula the area of the vent should equal that of the speaker cone, but for large drivers this may be impractical. An alternative formula for calculating the volume of the enclosure in litres (a litre is 1,000,000 cubic millimetres or 61 cubic inches), is:

$$V_b = 20 \ V_{as} \times Q_{ts}^{3.3}$$

in which V_{as} is the Thiele-Small parameter for the volume of air having the same compliance as the drive unit suspension, and Q_{ts} is the total driver damping factor. Obtaining the fractional power will pose no problem if you have a calculator with a x^y key.

While it is quite simple to work out the cabinet volume from this, the tube area and length are not, and as the two resonant systems must be matched, the dimensions are critical. The resonant frequency depends on the mass of air in the tube, and also its compliance. If mass was the only factor, the calculation would simply involve the volume of air in the tube, which is proportional to its area and length. Any combination of the two which produced the required volume would be satisfactory.

The complication is added by the compliance which is the inverse of the resistance offered to the rush of air trying to get through it. A wide short tube offers less resistance, and so has a higher compliance than a long narrow one, yet the mass of air could be the same in each.

A further factor is that a 'stub' of air develops beyond the end of the air in the pipe which moves it, so forming an invisible extension, increasing its mass. This effect varies with the length of the tube.

Unlike the totally sealed box in which size has little effect on the bass response as defined by the f_3 point, increasing the size of a reflex cabinet within limits, does give a lower f_3, and for a given diameter requires shorter tubes.

It may be thought that a *longer* tube containing more air would be needed to balance the larger mass of air in the larger enclosure, but the greater air mass is more easily compressed and so has a higher compliance. In the case of a tube open at both ends, a short tube offers less resistance to a volume of air flowing through it than a long one, and so has a higher compliance. Thus the compliance of both enclosure and tube is increased when the tube is shortened with an increase in cabinet size.

To illustrate the difference of f_3 response with cabinet size in litres and tube length, the chart on page 56 gives the figures for six typical loudspeakers. Optimum sizes for balance in each case is indicated. Cabinet size is in litres, tube diameter is 3 inches (75mm) in each case, and the length is in millimetres.

Not all systems use a tube, but rely on the air in the actual vent and that adjacent to it. With these, the vent is usually much larger than when a tube is employed.

Tuning the Port Without Maths

It can thus be seen why the calculation of dimensions of the port and its tube is by no means straightforward. Even when calculated, maker's prototypes often need modifications to tune them correctly. There is though a quite simple way of getting round the problem without recourse to complicated calculations, although a little patience is needed.

Cone diameter	12-inch		12-inch		12-inch		15-inch		15-inch		18-inch	
V_b litres	f_3	L	f_3	L	f_3	L	f_3	L	f_3	L	f_3	L
40			56	116	65	160						
50			54	82	60	118						
60	68	90	**50**	**60**	**52**	**90**						
70	61	69	45	44	49	69						
80	**58**	**54**	43	31	47	54						
90	54	42										
100	51	33										
110												
120							54	115	92	99		
130							52	103	80	85		
140							**50**	**93**	**74**	**74**		
150							48	84	72	64		
160							45	76	78	56	50	42
170											48	36
180											**44**	**31**
190											42	27
200											40	23

All the above systems used a 3-inch pipe and this is a convenient size that will serve for most projects, although some may need a larger diameter. A length of 3-inch plastic drain piping should be obtained and sawn up into sections starting at 4½ inches and reducing by half an inch down to 2 inches. This gives six experimental lengths, which should cover most cases if the cabinet volume has been correctly calculated.

Fit the drive unit into the cabinet and connect it to an amplifier with an a.c. ammeter connected in series with it. A cheap meter will do as it does not have to be accurate.

An audio oscillator is required to provide the test signal. This does not have to be anything fancy as long as its frequency can be varied around the resonant frequency of the system. An electronic keyboard instrument with a range well below the resonant frequency, can be used as an alternative to the oscillator although results are less accurate because its output cannot be swept smoothly over the frequency range. Feed a signal from the oscillator or keyboard into the amplifier input and adjust the amplifier gain and ammeter range to get a readable indication. Now starting well above the resonant frequency, slowly sweep the frequency of the oscillator or keyboard down to and below it.

The two resonant peaks will show up as dips in the current reading. The important thing is to get them both the same, if they are not equal the two resonant frequencies are not matched. Try different lengths of tube until one is found that gives equal dips. If none of them does so exactly, take the one that is next longer to the tube giving the best result, saw off a quarter of an inch and try it. If it is worse, saw of a quarter inch from the best-result tube and try that again. The dips should now be very close in size.

As an alternative to the ammeter a voltmeter can be connected across the speaker, in which case the peaks will show as peaks and not dips. The success of using a voltmeter depends on the amplifier and how much its output voltage is dependant on the load. If the peaks are barely discernible, connect a 5-watt (or larger) wire-wound resistor in series with the amplifier and speaker. Any value from 5 to 100 ohms will do.

Summary

The reflex enclosure enables a lower bass f_3 point to be obtained than the sealed box for a given driver, although this usually requires a larger cabinet, but not always.

Below this though, the bass roll-off is much more rapid. Control of the cone is less tight, resulting in ringing and spurious motion, which although undesirable for hi-fi, may not be thought so for a bass musical instrument, especially if the range of the instrument does not go much below the loudspeaker f_3 point.

To give some idea of the comparative performance of the same drivers in infinite baffle (IB) and reflex enclosures, the chart on the opposite page shows the optimum size for 6 sample drivers in each mode with the f_3 point of each in Hz.

Although designing a reflex enclosure poses problems, building one is quite straightforward providing the plans of a good design are followed. It is not too difficult to build one without a plan if first the volume is worked out from the chosen driver data, and then the pipe is adjusted for length as we have described.

It should be noted that not all manufacturers provide the necessary Thiele-Small parameters. Rarely are they available from those hailing from the Far East, so there is a lot to be said for choosing British-made units from whom the data is usually forthcoming.

Cone diameter	12-inch		12-inch		12-inch		15-inch		15-inch		18-inch	
V_b litres	IB	Ref	IB	Ref	IB	Ref	IB	Ref	IB	Ref	IB	Ref
60	85		89	50		52						
70		58										
80					74							
90												
100												
110							67			56		
120									84			
130												
140											55	
150								50				
160												
170												
180												46

Chapter 6

THE HORN

From ancient times the special properties of the horn as an acoustic amplifier have been appreciated and used. It was discovered early that a hollow animal horn would amplify the voice or make quite a loud musical sound, hence no doubt the origin of the name. It has been used widely in musical wind instruments, and also for public-address systems, for some hi-fi reproducers, and also electronic music.

The horn has one major advantage over all other types of speaker system. It also has one major disadvantage. To understand these we need to know just what effect a horn has. In the case of a loudspeaker cone we have a large mass impelled by a considerable force used to move a slice of air of the same area which is very light. This is like the proverbial sledgehammer being used to crack a walnut, or, driving a car at high speed along a flat road in bottom gear.

If the loudspeaker cone is placed at the beginning of a duct that has an increasing area along its length, it first moves a slice of air of small area. This moves an adjacent one of slightly larger area, which moves one that is larger still, and so on. The final large slice actuates the free air at the end of the duct.

Efficiency

Thus the action of the cone is smoothly and progressively matched to the eventual low impedance of the free air. As a result of this, remarkable efficiencies can be obtained of over 80% compared with less than 1% for most infinite baffle speakers. So the theoretical output can be well over eighty times that of a sealed box speaker, or conversely, quite a small amplifier of just a few watts would be more than adequate. It should be noted though that practical construction requirements for transportable musical instrument loudspeakers prevent the formation of a technically perfect horn, so efficiencies are much less than those theoretically obtainable. Even so outputs of two or three times that of a comparable

61

infinite baffle of reflex units can be obtained for the same power.

Flares

The manner by which the horn increases in area affects its performance. The simplest configuration is a cone, but it is by no means the best. Reflections can occur between the sides which cause interference and irregular frequency response as well as distortion. The ideal is an exponential horn by which the area increases according to an exponential law (Fig.15). This gives optimum air load matching and prevents internal reflections.

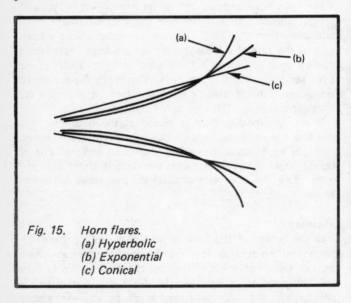

Fig. 15. Horn flares.
(a) Hyperbolic
(b) Exponential
(c) Conical

Because there is a mathematical law governing the expansion of area, it follows that there is a fixed relationship between the length of the horn and the size of the flare at its end. A large flare must have a long passage leading to it.

Another factor related to size is the frequency response. The shortest wavelength that the horn will reproduce is twice the diameter of the throat or start of the horn. The longest wavelength it will radiate is equal to twice the flare diameter. It is this last fact that gives rise to the big disadvantage. To obtain a response down to 100 Hz, a flare of 5.6 ft (1.7m) is required. For a 50 Hz response it would have to be 11.2 ft across.

The length of the horn needed for a specified flare and throat area is given by:

$$L = \frac{\log A - \log a}{f \log \epsilon} \quad 4,000$$

in which L is the length of the horn in cm; A is the area of the flare, and a the area of the throat in cm^2; f is the lowest frequency; log ϵ is 0.4343.

A horn following a hyperbolic area increase gives a response to a lower frequency than that of the exponential horn, but the roll-off below it is more rapid. The area increase from the throat is more gradual, so the sound pressure is greater there, to fall off more rapidly near the flare. This pressure variation along the length results in distortion being generated.

Throat Design
The throat needs to be of as small an area as practically possible in order to obtain a good high frequency response, because as we have already seen the shortest wavelength the horn will produce is twice the throat diameter. However, the cone needs to be larger than this in order that it will function effectively, so this means that the area immediately in front of the cone must narrow down to the start of the horn proper. A region of high pressure is thereby created in front of the cone which could cause it to respond in a non-linear fashion and so produce distortion. To avoid this the pressure is equalised by a sealed chamber placed behind the cone.

Another problem is that sound pressure from the central and outer areas of the cone could arrive at the centrally located throat at slightly different times because of the difference in spacing from it. Cancellation effects at various frequencies could thereby occur. This is prevented by introducing a plug with holes in it in front of the cone to delay some of the pressure waves so that they all arrive at the throat at the same time.

Horns for Musical Instruments

Most of the design details we have discussed relate to the long metal public-address horns often seen in sports stadia and other outdoor locations. We have done so in order to show what principles are involved and the problems that are encountered when attempting to squeeze a horn into a wooden cabinet.

For full-range domestic hi-fi loudspeakers a complicated arrangement of baffles form a flare passage of increasing area from the rear of the cone of a small bass driver to the eventual outlet port. The front of the driver faces directly outward, so it is said to be rear-loaded. A tweeter is used for the treble, which is radiated directly by the front of the speaker and so is not limited by the area of the throat or start of the passage.

The partitions do not have to be lagged, as the sound pressure waves do not impinge directly as they do with sealed enclosures, but travel parallel to them. In fact lagging would destroy the smooth progressive nature of the flare.

Owing to the high powers required for live musical auditorium work, a large driver is required and this prevents the use of a long flare of increasing area in a cabinet of manageable size. Some folding of the flare with internal baffles is used in a few models, but in most cases there is just a short straight flare from the cone to the front of the cabinet. Thus the theoretical effiency of the horn is greatly curtailed, but can be still two or three times that obtained from a reflex or infinite baffle for the same power.

As the length and width of the flare govern the lowest frequency that will be produced, the bass does not extend as deep as a reflex. However it can be extended by using barn doors (folding side panels) or stacking two or more units.

Chapter 7

TRANSMISSION-LINE LOUDSPEAKERS

The transmission-line or labyrinth type of enclosure has many advantages over other types of enclosure for domestic use, but like all the others has some practical disadvantages too. It consists of a long folded path formed by an arrangement of baffles within the cabinet that is filled with acoustically absorbent material, down which the rear wave is sent.

It gets its name from its similarity to a long cable used as a transmission-line which has such a high level of loss that most of a signal sent down it gets absorbed and very little appears at the far end. Any that remains is reflected back along the line and undergoes further loss on the return journey so that virtually nothing arrives back at the source. In the case of the rear sound from a loudspeaker cone, the loss is gradual, and there are no violent reflections or non-linear air resistance to the cone motion. Thus one of the major sources of distortion of the infinite baffle enclosure is eliminated.

In practice the end of the line is left open so that what is left of the rear wave escapes into free air. What happens then depends on the amount of absorbent in the line. If a minimal amount is included, a fairly strong rear wave emerges, but because of the time taken to travel along the line it is in phase with the front wave and so reinforces it. This occurs when the length of the line is a quarter of the wavelength of the emerging sound.

The effect is thus similar to that of the reflex enclosure but without the strong air and possible panel resonances. An air resonance does exist but it is damped by the absorbent material and so is of a much lower Q and thus produces less coloration. The reflex enclosure on the other hand must be undamped because its operation depends on resonance.

Like the reflex system though, the bass roll-off is rapid below the quarter-wavelength frequency which is usually chosen to be at the speaker cone resonant frequency. When so chosen, the cone excursion, as with the reflex speaker, is curtailed by the air load and so permits greater power handling and less distortion at that frequency.

If alternatively, the line is well filled with absorbent material, the emerging rear wave is weak and does little to reinforce the front wave. However, the roll-off is more gentle, and if the length of the line is made slightly longer than the quarter wavelength of the cone resonant frequency, the roll-off can be extended a little lower still.

The transmission-line enclosure behaves like an organ pipe, closed at one end and open at the other. As such it has a fundamental resonant frequency which can not only colour the reproduction by over-emphasis of that frequency, but as with all resonant objects, it stores energy and releases it after the signal has ceased so giving a spurious output. The design, therefore, is concerned with damping this resonance and its harmonic as much as possible.

One of the best examples of the transmission-line loudspeaker is the Kapellmeister which outperforms many larger and expensive models. It is fully described with constructional plans in the book BP256, *An Introduction to Loudspeakers and Enclosure Design*. Transmission-line units though are not generally employed for stage use because the high-power large drivers needed would require a long, large-area path which in turn would make the cabinet size and weight excessive. So although excellent for domestic use, it is rather impractical for the travelling musician.

Generally, auditorium loudspeakers for electronic musical instruments are either open-backed infinite baffle, reflex, or horn. Sometimes there is a combination of types such as a horn-loaded reflex. Transmission-line loudspeakers could be used for reinforcing acoustic instruments for which their lack of coloration would be ideal. They would be excellent for permanent installation in a concert hall for this purpose.

Chapter 8

CROSSOVER NETWORKS

It is common practice with full-range loudspeakers to employ separate drivers to handle the treble and bass frequencies, and sometimes the mid frequencies too. These are used for keyboard instruments and monitoring, but single instruments such as lead or bass guitars, have a limited frequency range and so are adequately served by a single driver or a pair in tandem.

An essential requirement in such multiple driver systems is a circuit for separating the frequency bands that feed the different drivers. These are known as *crossover networks* and consist of an arrangement of two basic components, a capacitor and an inductor or coil. In this chapter we will describe how these work and the features of various types. It is necessarily rather technical, but we will try to make it as understandable as possible to readers without a technical grounding.

Capacitive Reactance

Firstly, let us consider exactly what a basic capacitor is. It consists of two conductors having a large area in close proximity to each other. When a voltage source is connected across it, electrons are drawn from one surface and rush through the source to the other. There is thus a deficiency on the first and a surplus on the second. The capacitor is then said to be charged and if the source is disconnected, a voltage equal to that of the source can be measured across the capacitor.

Charging a capacitor is not like filling a bottle, in that once it is full it will accept no more. If the source voltage is increased, the charge will increase right to the point when the insulation between the surfaces breaks down. It is more like inflating a balloon which will take more and more until finally it bursts.

At the instant of connecting the capacitor to the source, the current flow is large as there is virtually no opposition to it. But as it becomes charged, its rising internal potential

67

opposes that of that source thus reducing the charging current. This decreases until the internal potential and source voltage are equal, at which point it ceases. The charging curve is therefore not linear but exponential.

If removed from the source and applied to an external load, the capacitor will discharge in a similar manner, the current decreasing as the potential falls. Even without an external load a capacitor will discharge itself in time because of internal leakage through the imperfect insulation.

If a capacitor is partly charged, and then the source voltage is reversed, it will discharge and begin to charge to the opposite polarity. If the source is again reversed before the recharge is complete, it will discharge once more and start a further charge to its original polarity. This process can be kept going indefinitely, with current flowing in and out at each polarity reversal.

So, an a.c. source will keep current flowing, providing the reversals occur before the capacitor is fully charged. It should be noted that as the maximum current flows before the voltage starts to rise, maximum current and voltage do not occur at the same time. The current leads the voltage by 90°.

If the reversals are very rapid, charging and discharging will always take place at the start of the curve where the current is greatest. If reversals are slow, the capacitor will be well charged and the current be reducing before the next reversal comes. So, the average current passing through a capacitor is dependent on how rapid the reversals are. In other words, the magnitude of the current depends on the frequency of the a.c. source, the higher the frequency, the greater the current.

It also depends on the size of the capacitor. One having a large capacitance takes longer to charge and discharge, and so will still be operating at the early high-current portion of its curve at the slower low frequencies. The larger the capacitance then, the higher the current.

Both frequency and capacitance are therefore factors governing the current flow through a capacitor. They are combined in the property termed *Capacitive Reactance*, symbol X_c, which is to a capacitor what resistance is to a resistor, hence the unit is the ohm. The formula is:

$$\frac{1}{2\pi fC}$$

where f = frequency in Hz, and C = capacitance in farads. For microfarads the formula becomes:

$$\frac{10^6}{2\pi fC}$$

The capacitor thus offers a high impedance to low frequency signals and a low impedance to high frequencies so enabling it to be used as an element in frequency selective filter circuits.

Inductive Reactance

When a current flows through a straight wire, a circular magnetic field surrounds it which is made up of individual lines of force. If the wire is wound in the form of a coil, the lines link up to produce a concentrated field which form loops passing radially through the centre of the coil and around its exterior.

When the current starts to flow, the field does not appear instantaneously, but rapidly builds up from zero. Likewise when the current ceases, it collapses. In both instances the lines of force cut across the windings of the coil. It is this action that gives the coil its peculiar property.

Whenever a magnetic line of force cuts across a conductor, it induces an electromotive force (EMF) in it. This is the principle on which all electric generators depend. It matters not whether the conductor moves or the magnetic field, nor does it matter whether the field is produced by a permanent magnet or an electromagnet.

It follows that when the field produced by a coil builds up or collapses and so cuts across its own windings, an EMF is induced in them. This always *opposes* the original voltage that produced the current, because its polarity is opposite to it. Thus the effective voltage acting in the circuit is that of the applied voltage minus the self-induced voltage.

In the case of a d.c. supply, the effect is momentary. When the current starts to flow, the opposing EMF inhibits it so that it builds up slowly to its maximum. After this, the field is stationary and so has no effect. On removing the applied voltage the EMF generated by the collapsing field tries to perpetuate the current. Quite high voltages can be induced by the collapsing field.

With a.c., the field is constantly changing and so the current is continuously opposed. This is the property which is termed *Inductive Reactance.* Because the current builds up slowly it lags behind the applied voltage by 90° so maximum current and voltage do not occur at the same time.

The opposing or back EMF is proportional to the speed of the changing field, being highest when the speed is greatest. As the rate of change increases with frequency, it follows that the reactance is not constant but increases as the frequency rises.

It is also dependant on the inductance of the coil. This is a rather complex factor depending on the total number of turns, the turns per inch, length and diameter of the coil and the number of layers. Also affecting inductance is whether the coil is air-cored, is iron-cored (increases inductance) or is brass-cored (decreases inductance). The latter applies when brass slugs are used for tuning r.f. coils. The formula for inductive reactance is:

$$X_L = 2\pi fL$$

in which X_L is in ohms, f = frequency in Hz, and L is inductance in henries.

The inductive action of a coil is reduced by its d.c. resistance so dividing the reactance by the resistance gives a quality (Q) factor. The formula then is:

$$Q = \frac{X_L}{R} .$$

Thus at low frequencies the inductor offers minimum impedance, but at high frequencies the impedance is also high.

Along with the capacitor which has the opposite effect, it thus affords a means of separating an audio signal into bands suitable for driving multi-speaker systems.

First-order Network

Combinations of inductors and capacitors are arranged to provide *low-pass*, *high-pass*, or *band-pass* characteristics. These are used to supply the bass driver, treble unit, and mid-range speaker respectively.

The simplest circuit is of a single capacitor connected in series with the tweeter. This prevents low frequencies reaching the tweeter which would seriously damage it. Both low and high frequencies are fed to the bass unit which will reproduce some of the highs due to cone flexure. Having two speakers reproducing high frequencies in close lateral proximity will result in interference at certain angles, reinforcement taking place at some frequencies and cancellation at others. Because of this the circuit is used only in cheap radio units, but it can be and is used effectively with co-axial speakers where the tweeter is mounted within the bass cone.

To avoid interference effects, an inductor is connected in series with the bass unit which filters out the high frequencies, so we have a capacitor feeding the tweeter and an inductor supplying the woofer. This is known as a *first-order* network, each leg attenuating the signal outside of its pass range at the rate of *6 dB per octave* (Fig.16).

The point where they overlap is known as the *crossover frequency* and the values of the components are chosen so that at this point the response of each driver is -3 dB or at half power. As we saw earlier, current through a capacitor leads the voltage, whereas it lags through an inductor. In the first-order network, the lead and lag is $45°$ in each case giving a $90°$ total. However, these compensate acoustically to produce an in-phase signal from the drivers at the crossover frequency (Fig.17). The two half-power signals thus add to produce full power and so the response through the crossover region is flat. The formulae for calculating the theoretical values are:

$$L = \frac{Z\,10^3}{2\pi\,f_c} \qquad C = \frac{10^6}{2\pi f_c Z}$$

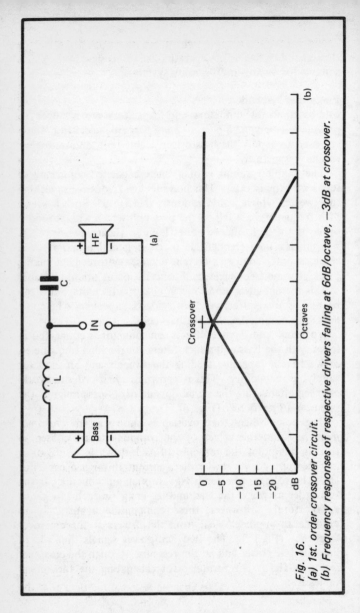

Fig. 16.
(a) 1st. order crossover circuit.
(b) Frequency responses of respective drivers falling at 6dB/octave, −3dB at crossover.

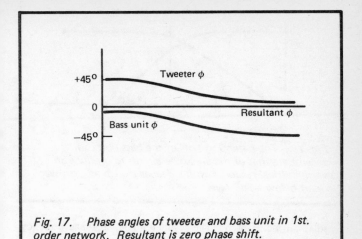

*Fig. 17. Phase angles of tweeter and bass unit in 1st.
order network. Resultant is zero phase shift.*

in which L is the inductance in millihenries; C is the
capacitance in microfarads; Z is the speaker impedance; and
f_c is the crossover frequency.

There is a snag here though. The 6 dB per octave roll-off
is too gentle. It means that at two octaves from the crossover
point, both drivers are handling a −12 dB signal that is outside
of their respective bands, while at three octaves there is still a
−18 dB signal.

The problem arises when the natural frequency roll-off of
one of the drivers coincides with that of the filter. Then the
total roll-off for that driver is augmented and made steeper.
So the two roll-offs for the two drivers are asymmetrical,
one being steeper than the other. This produces a power
level of less than −3 dB for the affected driver at the crossover
frequency resulting in a dip in the response (Fig.18).

A further snag lies in the fact that the tweeter will be fed
with substantial proportions of the bass signal which would
not only produce distortion due to overloading it, but could
result in damage. Yet another undesirable factor is that the
tweeter resonant frequency which should be kept below the
crossover point and so out of the range it is required to

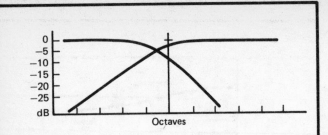

Fig. 18.   The natural roll-off of the bass unit can accentuate that of the crossover circuit to produce an asymmetrical response with a deeper trough at crossover point below −3dB level.

handle, can be excited. The result is a peak at that frequency which is generally in the mid-frequency range.

Higher Orders
The solution to these problems is to use filters having a sharper roll-off. A 12 dB per octave characteristic can be obtained by adding a capacitor across the bass driver and an inductor across the tweeter. This circuit is a *second-order* network (Fig.19), and it is also known as an L-filter because the series and parallel components form an L when drawn in a circuit diagram.

The disadvantage is that the phase difference between the drivers is 180°, which produces a dip in the response at the crossover frequency. This can be avoided by reverse connecting the tweeter, but then a hump is produced instead. A further effect is that all the high frequencies are in an opposite phase relationship to the low, compared to what they were in the original signal.

When reproducing sound, a musical instrument that is rich in harmonics such as the cello, may have its fundamental and perhaps it second harmonic reproduced by the bass driver and the higher harmonics by the tweeter. Having the tweeter reversed thus changes the relationship and subsequent resultant sound pressure waveform. While the evidence is that this seems to have little audible effect, it is a departure from the exact original.   This matters less when the loudspeaker is producing sound from an electronic source as there is no question of fidelity to an original sound.

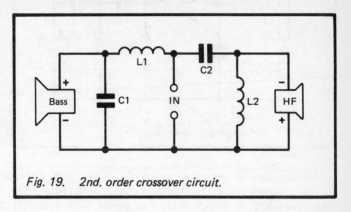

Fig. 19.   2nd. order crossover circuit.

Sometimes a resistor is included in series with the tweeter and its series capacitor. This is done to attenuate its output when the tweeter sensitivity is greater than that of the bass driver which is often the case. Sensitivities are thus matched to give a uniform response. A bonus effect of this is to reduce the amount of current lead through the tweeter due to the capacitor, and thus the phase difference between the two drivers.

Further components can be added to form a *third-order* network. This has an extra inductor in series with the bass unit and an extra capacitor in series with the tweeter. The circuit for each section looks like a T so it is often called a T-filter (Fig.20). The roll-off slope in this case is 18 dB per octave (Fig.21). The formulae for calculating theoretical values are:

$$L_1 = 3L_2 = 2L_3 = \frac{3Z\ 10^3}{4\pi f_c}$$

and

$$C_1 = 2C_2 = \frac{2C_3}{3} = \frac{20^6}{3\pi f_c Z}\ .$$

75

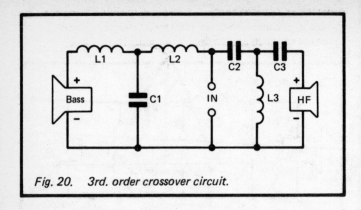

Fig. 20.   3rd. order crossover circuit.

Adding another capacitor across the bass driver and a further inductor across the tweeter forms a fourth-order filter. This looks like the Greek letter π in circuit form and so is called a π filter (Fig.22). It has a roll-off of 24 dB per octave. As with the second-order filter there is a 180° phase reversal so the tweeter can be reverse connected unless other components are included which affect the phasing. Fourth-order filters are rarely used for crossover networks; second and third being the most common.

The previous formulae assume that the driver impedance is constant which is not the case, it varies with frequency and resonances. They should therefore be considered as a starting point, and the values be modified according to the response of the driver. Sometimes irregularities in the response of one of the drivers can be partly compensated for by extra components, usually resistors across or in series with the main filter components, but additional inductors and capacitors are often used as well (Fig.23). It is thus possible to achieve a very flat response for a particular pair of drivers and enclosure. With so many variable factors the design frequently needs to be carried out by computer.

For any published design therefore, neither the type of drivers nor values of the network should be changed. They have, or should have been, carefully optimized. It follows that choosing a pair of drivers at random, then using an off-the-shelf crossover is very unlikely to give satisfactory results.

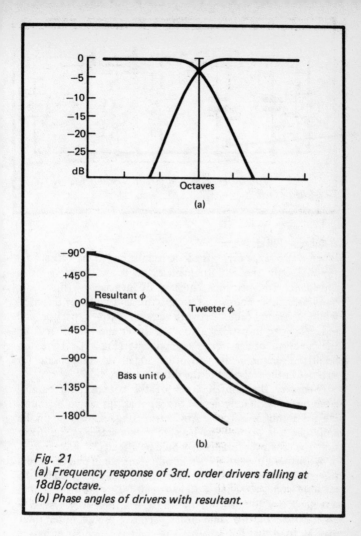

Fig. 21
(a) Frequency response of 3rd. order drivers falling at 18dB/octave.
(b) Phase angles of drivers with resultant.

However, some speaker manufacturers do little more than that, and certain ones have been known to substitute a quite different driver with no modification of the crossover filter at all, for the sole reason of lower cost.

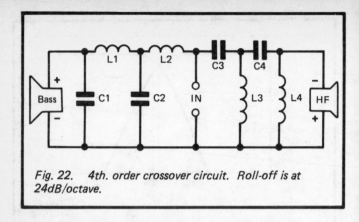

Fig. 22. 4th. order crossover circuit. Roll-off is at 24dB/octave.

Band-pass Filters

When a mid-range driver is added it must be fed via a filter that supplies only the mid frequencies, so it must offer a rising impedance to both high and low frequencies. A first-order band-pass filter consists of a capacitor and inductor in series, while a second-order network has an extra capacitor and inductor, one in parallel across the driver and the other from the junction of the series components (Fig.24). Here too additional components are often added to compensate for vagaries in the response of the driver.

Whatever the configuration of the network, no parallel component is directly across the input as this would be shunting the amplifier output. Any attenuating resistors are on the amplifier side of the filter because if connected on the driver side, the crossover frequency would be affected.

A further convention is that all inputs are in parallel across the amplifier output so that each section may be considered a separate and independent filter circuit. This means that it is not necessary for both or the three, if a three-way system is used, to be of the same order. Thus a second-order filter may be used for the treble unit to limit the amount of bass it will be fed, while only a first-order circuit is used for the bass driver, as it may be considered less important to limit the high frequencies it handles. While this may result in some interference effects as we have seen, it reduces the phase difference and the effects of 'ringing'.

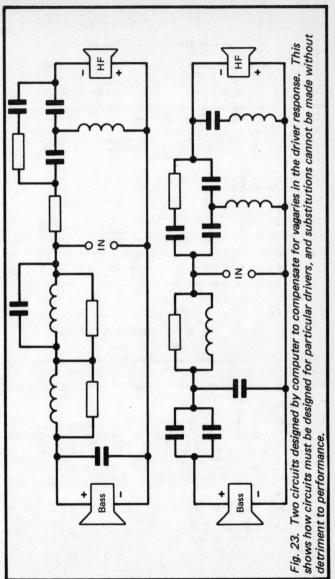

Fig. 23. Two circuits designed by computer to compensate for vagaries in the driver response. This shows how circuits must be designed for particular drivers, and substitutions cannot be made without detriment to performance.

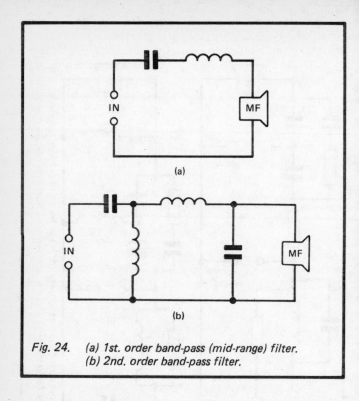

Fig. 24. (a) 1st. order band-pass (mid-range) filter.
(b) 2nd. order band-pass filter.

Components

The capacitors used are generally in the range of $1 - 10 \mu F$. Polarized electrolytics with a positive and negative connection should not be used as the signal is pure a.c. Furthermore, they have a wide tolerance and so a precise value cannot be obtained. Non-polarized electrolytics can be used, but other types are preferable.

It may then be wondered why a polarized electrolytic is used for coupling the output stage to the speaker circuit. The reason is that there is d.c. on the output-stage side, on which the signal is superimposed. So the actual voltage across the capacitor never reverses. Its value is not critical because it is not in a frequency selective circuit.

The inductors can be either air-cored or ferrite cored. The ferrite components are smaller because they are magnetically more efficient, most of the generated flux being concentrated in the windings by the core. The disadvantage is that it is possible for the core to saturate at high signal levels thereby varying the inductance, hence also the impedance. The result is harmonic distortion and changing of the crossover characteristics.

Air-cored inductors do not suffer from this possibility, but they are larger and heavier. A problem can arise from the large leakage field which can interact with any other inductor within range and so introduce mutual coupling between them. The effects can be strange and unpredictable. All coils but especially air-cored ones, should be mounted well apart, and if possible with their axes at right-angles.

A printed circuit board is the usual method of interconnecting the components, but however the components are connected they should be fixed securely with no possibility of adjacent ones touching and thereby able to produce buzzes or rattles when subject to high level sound waves.

Side-effects

Like so many other things crossover networks are not an unmixed blessing, they have many undesirable side-effects. Capacitors and inductors store energy, then release it when the applied signal ceases. It doesn't stop though, but surges backwards and forwards in the circuit like water in a bucket that has been given a sideways jolt. So, if a sound should cease abruptly, it doesn't, the components in the crossover make it decay slowly. This effect is called *ringing*.

This spurious oscillation can be fed back into the earlier stages of an amplifier by the negative feedback circuit, and because of phase shifts be amplified and arrive back at the loudspeaker considerably worsened.

The crossover network also constitutes an impedance in series with the loudspeaker and amplifier output. Now we saw earlier that spurious cone motion is damped by the back voltage it generates producing a current, which in turn creates a magnetic field in the coil windings that opposes the original spurious motion. Any series impedance restricts the current and so reduces the amount of damping.

Thus the crossover network adds distortion and reduces the tight control that the amplifier should have over the motion of the loudspeaker cone. The availability of excellent full-range loudspeakers that exploit the phenomena of cone flexure described in Chapter 2, really makes the network an out-dated evil that deserves to be thrown out of the hi-fi window! However, for electronic musical instrument loudspeakers the situation is somewhat different. Fidelity to an original sound is not in question and some distortion of the generated waveform may actually be welcomed. We will explore this more fully in a later chapter.

Chapter 9

ABSORBENTS

Absorbents are used for two main purposes in loudspeaker enclosures: firstly to damp panel vibrations, and secondly to damp internal air resonances. The panels of enclosures that are totally sealed or have a small vent to function in the reflex mode, are subject to large pressure differences between their internal and external surfaces. These can cause them to warp in sympathy and thereby themselves radiate sound. Such sound is coloured by the resonances of the panels and so adds distortion to that radiated by the loudspeaker cone.

Panel Damping

A heavy and dense absorbent layer fixed to the internal panel surfaces considerably damps any tendency to sympathetic vibration. A comparatively light panel heavily lagged has proved less prone to vibration than a more substantial panel only lightly damped. Generally, the thicker the layer, the lower the frequency it will effectively absorb. As it is at the lower and mid frequencies that the panels resonate, only a thick or very dense layer is of any use. Various materials have been used for this purpose, but among the best so far discovered are bituminous pads.

All panels of infinite baffle speakers should be internally lagged with these but not those of reflex cabinets as the resonance effects on which the enclosure depends could be damped. Transmission-line and folded horn partitions do not need lagging, and the operation of the horn in particular would be impaired by it.

The rear panel in the infinite baffle and reflex enclosures is especially prone to trouble, as high pressure waves can be reflected back to the loudspeaker, and right through the cone which is virtually acoustically transparent. At frequencies when the depth of the cabinet is equal to a quarter and three-quarter wavelengths, cancellation occurs, and at those corresponding to a half and whole wavelengths there is reinforcement. A series of dips and peaks result, some accompanied by severe distortion.

Particular attention should therefore be paid to the lagging of the rear wall to avoid this effect, and even reflex enclosures which are normally unlagged should have rear wall damping.

Air Resonances

The three enclosure dimensions of a sealed enclosure have their fundamental air resonance frequencies along with harmonics (Fig.25). To damp these, absorbent material needs to be located at the positions of maximum air motion or the antinodes.

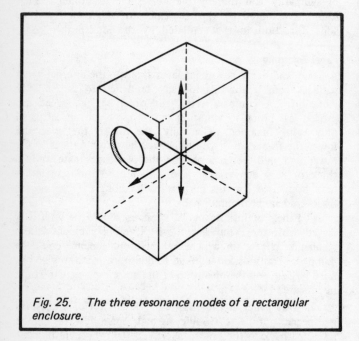

Fig. 25.   The three resonance modes of a rectangular enclosure.

These antinodes are spread across numerous points in all dimensions so the most practical course with a small enclosure is to completely fill it with absorbent. With large enclosures such as used for live auditorium work, the problem is to avoid compression of the lower layers by the weight of the upper ones. One way of overcoming this is to fill the lower area with several rolls of material standing vertically, then lay a horizontal roll across the top.

Reflex enclosures should not have any absorbent filling other than on the rear wall, as the air resonance is essential for their operation. The horn likewise should also be without absorbent in the flare.

Transmission-line enclosures need absorbent in the air passages, though not fixed to the baffles. The purpose is to 'lose' the rear wave as far as possible. As the transmission-line behaves as a closed pipe it has a strong fundamental resonance along with odd harmonics. The second function of the absorbent is therefore to damp these resonant modes. Extra density at the antinodal positions serve to accomplish this.

Materials

A variety of materials have been used for enclosure damping. Polyurethane foam is a convenient one as it can be obtained in various sizes, blocks and sheet. Glass fibre has been used, but is not recommended. Its acoustic absorbent properties are inferior to other materials, and it can be a health hazard to work with. However, if nothing else is available, it can be used.

Long-fibre wool is considered the best material of all, but being loose, it is not easy to use and some method of retaining it in place must be devised. It suffers more than most from the problem of compacting under its own weight where large volumes are used. Another factor which must be considered is the need for moth-proofing if the enclosure is open, such as with a transmission-line.

The material most generally used because of its convenience and acoustic properties is bonded cellulose acetate fibre, commonly known as BAF wadding. It comes in sheets of 1-inch or 2-inch thickness, usually 3 ft wide, and can be rolled up to form large wads or laid out in several thicknesses. It is quite easy to cut. It is springy and so can be compressed with extra thicknesses at antinodal points, but its density is normally about right for general filling. Over compression can result in too great a density with a reduction of the actual air volume.

85

BAF should be used wherever possible. It is supplied by the specialist loudspeaker firms such as Wimslow Audio and is available by mail order. It may be difficult to obtain locally, as it is only specialist shops that stock it.

Adiabatic Propagation

When a sound wave travels through air it is assisted by self-generated heat. It is a well-known fact that pressure produces heat. So the regions of high pressure within the wave generate corresponding regions of higher temperature. These expand, thereby increasing the pressure and producing more heat. The sound wave quickly passes and the regions at different temperatures soon merge, so there is no lasting effect at any static point in the path of the sound wave.

However, the pressure wave carries a wave of higher temperature with it, the region of high pressure always being at a higher temperature than the mean air temperature. Now the velocity of a sound wave varies with temperature, being greater at higher values. So the velocity of the pressure wave is actually increased by its self-generated heat. The propagation is said to be *adiabatic*, which means impervious to heat change. As this is the normal way whereby sound is propagated it is allowed for in our acoustic calculations and it is not usually necessary to consider it. It is when conditions differ from this, that we need to take it into account.

Isothermal Propagation

When a sound pressure wave travels through a medium which conducts heat more readily than air, which is a very poor conductor, the higher temperature regions lose heat more quickly to the surrounding lower temperature areas. Thus the temperature is not maintained and in fact never reaches the value that it would have done in air. The result is that the sound velocity is slower than in air. The condition is termed *isothermal* which literally means 'of the same heat' as adjacent regions do not have the temperature differences of the adiabatic condition.

Absorbent material such as BAF, although not seeming to be a good conductor of heat, conducts it better than air. So sound generated in a loudspeaker enclosure filled with an absorbent is propagated in partly isothermal conditions. It is thereby slowed down.

This has a useful bonus effect. The time taken to travel across a filled enclosure is longer, so the enclosure therefore appears to be larger to the sound wave. We thus get the same effect from an absorbent filled enclosure than we would from a larger one that was unfilled.

Unfortunately the difference is not large; for a fully isothermal state, the reduction in sound velocity is $\sqrt{2}$ or 1.414, giving the effect of an enclosure that is much larger in volume. This would reduce the resonant frequency to about 0.833 of its former value, a very useful reduction. However, the effect of the absorbent is to create an only partly isothermal condition, much depending on the material and the packing density. It is interesting to speculate what effect fine copper wires spun into the material may have in increasing the effect to nearly full isothermal propagation.

Chapter 10

CHOOSING THE LOUDSPEAKER

In the previous chapters we have explored the various types of loudspeaker enclosure and the drivers themselves. From these it can be gathered that some units are more suitable for one purpose than another, and also that the choice will be governed by the sort of sound you want to project. We will now draw these threads together and see what options there are for the choice.

The first observation as we have noted before, is that musical instrument loudspeakers are quite different from hi-fi models. The first are used for the *production* of sound, the second for *re-production*. In the latter case, all forms of distortion must be kept to a minimum and the response to all frequencies must be equal. The loudspeaker is neutral, contributing nothing and omitting nothing.

With electronic instruments there is no original sound to reproduce, the loudspeaker IS part of the instrument. So, as the sounding box of an acoustic guitar adds overtones and resonances, thereby transforming the rather uninteresting twanging of a steel string into a thing of beauty, so can the loudspeaker with the electronic instrument.

This means that the design and construction is not as critical as it is for a hi-fi unit. We do not have to be concerned with avoiding all distortion and eliminating all resonances. So, whereas each hi-fi cabinet should be specifically designed for specific drivers and crossover circuit, we have rather more latitude. In fact, if we can beg, borrow, or afford to buy several different drivers, we can try them in turn in a particular cabinet to find the one that gives us the sound we want. Many designs permit the easy replacement of the driver for that very purpose.

Range

Another factor which simplies the design, is the range of frequencies to be covered. Musical instrument loudspeakers need cover only the range of the instrument with some treble

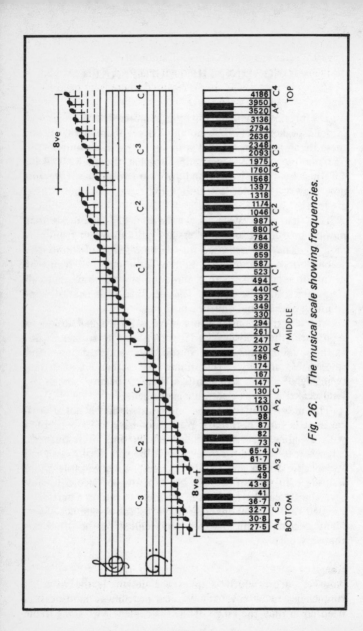

Fig. 26. The musical scale showing frequencies.

extension to produce overtones and harmonics. Hi-fi units have to cover the whole range of audibility from deepest bass to highest treble overtone, although many are deficient in bass. If then a limited range only is required, there is no need to use multiple drivers with crossover networks.

For some applications full-range loudspeakers are required. These are needed for wide-range keyboard instruments, and also for stage monitors. Figure 26 shows the musical scale with frequency values. The frequency range of a particular instrument can thus be determined from this, and therefore the range required for the loudspeaker.

Power output is much greater than with domestic units, so the drivers chosen must be capable of handling it. Also, the cabinets themselves must be stoutly constructed with no loose parts or wooden sections of inadequate thickness that could vibrate. While this is true of domestic loudspeakers, the high powers involved with musical loudspeakers make it even more important. We shall go further into this in the next chapter.

Now we shall look at individual instruments to see what can be employed with them.

Lead Guitar
The frequency range is from 196 Hz (G_1) to 1,568 Hz (G^3), a span of three octaves. Clearly a loudspeaker with a deep bass response is unnecessary, so a reflex is unsuitable. Nor is an infinite baffle needed, although one can be used if desired. An open-backed unit — acoustically not physically — is easy to make and as it contributes little to the tone compared to sealed enclosures, can be made in almost any reasonable size or shape providing it is not square, with the drive unit set in the centre.

It is important to note that an open-backed cabinet housing any loudspeaker designed for sealed-cabinet operation, should never be used to produce bass. These drivers have a weak suspension as they rely on the springiness of the air to maintain the cone in position; that is why they are often called acoustic suspension drivers. At mid and high frequencies these are adequately loaded if operated in a reasonably sized open-backed cabinet. At bass frequencies they are not, and would be damaged if bass frequencies were applied.

Although acoustically termed 'open-backed' the cabinet needs a back to protect the drive unit during transit. It can be made acoustically transparent by drilling a large number of small holes over it. The back then offers some acoustic resistance and an extra degree of loading.

The driver should be a 10- or 12-inch unit, ideally with in-built distortion and non-linearities to add the timbre. Paper surround, that is the cone pleated at the edge and joined directly to the frame, is the most suitable to achieve these effects, as there is thereby no absorption of cone ripples at the rim. These are reflected back across the cone to produce standing waves and cone break-up. Drivers are available with paper surrounds that are designed specially for the lead guitar, one range made by Celestion (at the time of writing) has three models, the *Vintage*, the *Classic* and the *Modern Lead*. These each have different distortions and resonances resulting in different characteristic sounds.

Over the frequency range of the fundamentals of the three units, the response is fairly even and similar. It is in the higher frequencies from 1,600 Hz to 6 kHz, that the peaks and troughs occur which distinguish them.

Power handling can be increased by mounting two drivers connected in parallel in the same cabinet. No crossover circuit is required because they are working over the same range of frequencies. This affords an opportunity to experiment by trying different drivers together to obtain a unique sound.

Bass Guitar

The requirements for the bass are quite different from those of the lead guitar. Frequency range is 41 Hz (E_3) to 261 Hz (middle C), so loudspeakers producing the deepest bass are necessary, with very little treble if any. Ideally, the loudspeaker should go down to 41 Hz, the lowest note.

It should be noted that the lower limit quoted by some manufacturers can be quite optimistic. It is governed by the resonant frequency of the cone, below which the response falls off by 12 dB per octave for sealed enclosures. However, that frequency is raised by the effect of the air in the enclosure, and small enclosures raise it more than large ones.

So, the actual resonant frequency is always higher with sealed enclosures than the quoted free air resonance. As it is common practice to specify a response some 10 Hz below the quoted resonance, the specified bass response is thus likely to be optimistic. With reflex units the bass is extended and is more like that quoted, but it drops off rapidly by some 24 dB per octave below resonance.

Many driver units that are supplied for use with bass instruments do not extend down to 40 Hz, but tail off around 60 Hz, half an octave higher. This does not mean that they will not produce lower notes. The response does not end abruptly at the specified frequency, there is still some output at lower frequencies though it is limited.

The main factor though is that the fundamental frequency of most vibrating strings is accompanied by large amounts of second and third harmonics with diminishing amounts of higher ones. The fundamental thus provides only a small part of the total energy of the note, and if cut out altogether is hardly missed. The human ear seems able to fill in missing fundamentals otherwise transistor radios would seem to reproduce no bass at all!

So, bass loudspeakers with a response to only 60 Hz or thereabouts will perform satisfactorily. However, for the maximum effect at the deep bass notes, it is desirable to have a response down to 40 Hz. This is best achieved by means of a reflex loudspeaker. If two or more bass loudspeaker cabinets are stacked, the bass response goes lower. Two will drop it by about 10 Hz, and four by 20 Hz. This is an expensive way though of getting deep bass, it is cheaper to use larger drivers and cabinets. However, the increased bass response is a bonus if a stack is to be used for very high powers at large gatherings such as open air concerts.

For a full deep bass with full production of the fundamentals 15- or 18-inch drivers are needed. However, some have a preference for using 12- or even 10-inch drivers to get a faster response with more attack, fitting four to a single reflex cabinet to get a reasonable bass response. So the choice is between deep bass or plenty of attack.

The main function of the bass instrument is to give support and backing to the lead, so it does not need to have peaks and resonances to give it a distinctive sound. Many players prefer it to be smooth and with a uniform response over its range. To achieve this the driver cone should not have a paper edge surround but be of the cloth surround type.

All the large bass units made by Celestion have cloth surrounds. However, some bass players may wish to have a brighter tone, and for these Fane make 15- and 18-inch drivers with paper edges. Going to the other extreme, all drivers made by McKenzie, including their 10- and 12-inch models for lead guitars, have cambric surrounds, so their lead models do not have the in-built coloration of the Celestion drivers.

Altai manufacture some bass units with resonant frequencies in the region of 20–30 Hz and so capable of producing bass down to those frequencies with suitable enclosures. They have rubber surrounds which give even less colouration than cloth. However they are much less sensitive, needing around three times the power of the cloth and paper types for the same sound output. As there is no need for the bass response to go below the lowest note of the instrument, the low sensitivity rather excludes them from the choice for this purpose.

Vocal

The human singing voice ranges from about 73 Hz, the lowest note of a bass, to 1,046, the top C of the soprano. However, pop and cabaret singers have a much more restricted range than that. A loudspeaker for vocal use obviously needs little bass response and would seem to need little treble either. However, harmonics up to around 5 or 6 kHz need to be reproduced to give intelligibility, and preserve the character of the voice. It may be noted in passing that female voices, although having higher-pitched fundamentals, have fewer harmonics than the male, and so do not extend as far up the frequency spectrum. This limited harmonic content is why female voices usually sound softer, whereas the male with a large number of harmonics sounds harder and more incisive.

It is also the reason why male voices are more understandable to the hard of hearing, not because they are louder, but because they have more harmonics that give greater clarity. So for announcements in unfavourable conditions, a male announcer is the best.

The reproduction needs to be uncoloured and without distortion. Reverberation may well be added at the amplifier, but the loudspeaker itself should reproduce no more or less than what goes into it.

The open-backed cabinet suggested for the lead guitar would be very suitable here as this gives a good, low distortion reproduction lacking only in bass which for vocals we do not need. The stricture about using such a cabinet for bass must be strictly observed. Full-range infinite baffle loudspeakers are sometimes used, although they are not really necessary.

A paper-edged lead guitar driver should not be used because of the in-built distortions. It should have a cloth or rubber surround rather than paper.

Keyboard

The type of loudspeaker most suitable for keyboard instruments depends a lot on the instrument itself, particularly its range. A large electronic organ may have pedal notes going down to C_4 which has a frequency of 16.3 Hz, but there are many keyboards that have a more modest bass range.

Another factor to consider is the likely size of the audience and auditorium. Very large audiences would require a stack of separate bass, middle and treble units, whereas smaller conclaves could be well served by one or two full-range loudspeakers.

As all the varied tone colours have been carefully achieved by the design of the internal electronic circuits, no extra modification is required from the loudspeaker, even though it is part of the instrument. In fact, any distortion would detract from the instrument's tonal character.

So the loudspeakers must be up to hi-fi standards. For the smaller audience, one or two full-range units going down to, or near, the lowest note in the range of the instrument, will be needed. The treble range of most keyboard instruments extends an octave or more higher than that of the lead guitar, and many of their stops give effects that are rich in high order harmonics. The loudspeaker response must therefore go high enough to produce them, which can be achieved with a suitable tweeter.

The tweeter must have a lower frequency limit which overlaps the highest frequency produced by the bass unit. The crossover is usually 3 kHz. Tweeters that respond down to this frequency often lose a little at the top end but this should not cause undue concern. A response up to 16 kHz is quite adequate as human hearing does not go any higher, and it is unlikely that the majority of the audience can hear even this high, especially if they are frequent attenders at high-powered rock concerts or discos! Tweeters are often advertised though, with a response up to 20 kHz and in some cases even beyond.

A more important specification for a tweeter is its polar response, that is the angle over which it disperses sound. A tweeter diaphragm propagates high frequencies in a narrow conical beam with about a 60° dispersion angle. A rectangular horn fitted to the front extends the side angle to some 90° at the expense of the vertical which is reduced to around 40° depending on the dimensions of the horn. Another type is the bullet tweeter which as its name implies has a bullet-shaped diffuser surrounding a circular horn in front of the diaphragm. This radiates a conical beam over a 90° angle.

A wider dispersion can be obtained from a unit fitted with a slot diffractor, such as one model made by Fane. This has a horizontal spread of over 120° with a vertical one of 50°.

It is obvious that in a wide auditorium, those sitting at the front sides are at a very wide angle to a loudspeaker standing on stage. They will get no high frequencies at all, and even those nearer the centre will get few unless they are within the range of the tweeter. So horizontal dispersion is an important factor. A wide angle is usually necessary, but as the sound energy is thus spread, the tweeter has less 'throw' than when the sound is concentrated into a narrower beam.

High frequencies are attenuated to a greater extent than low frequencies when they pass through air. As they are radiated out from the loudspeakers on the stage, they also undergo greater absorption by the clothing of the audience. So, the sound reaching the back rows will be deficient in the highest harmonics and so have lost its attack and crispness.

The solution for large audiences is to have an array of tweeters in an arc, mounted in a separate box from the bass unit. This gives a wide dispersion while retaining the long throw of individual units. The spacing and angling of the units can be critical if mutual interference is to be avoided. A practical design appears in the last chapter.

Wide vertical dispersion is unnecessary unless a balcony is to be served from the same rig. So for a smaller auditorium, a full-range unit containing a wide-angle tweeter with restricted vertical range could be adequate. For a medium-sized hall, two such units placed either side of the keyboard, angled slightly outward, should give good coverage.

If the bass unit is 15−18 inches and goes really low it is unlikely to perform very well in the middle frequencies, so a mid-range unit will also be required. However, deep bass can be obtained from 12-inch rubber edged drivers which also have quite a reasonable mid response. The Altai units mentioned previously are an example. As mentioned before though, rubber surround units need more power to give the same output as a cloth edge.

One reason for using a mid-range unit is the doppler effect at higher powers. A sound source moving toward the listener seems to have a higher pitch than the same source moving away. The effect is commonly heard with ambulance sirens. A loudspeaker cone moves toward and away from the listener each cycle of sound it produces. If it is doing this at a low frequency, and at the same time radiating a higher tone, that high note will vary in pitch in sympathy with the lower one due to doppler effect.

This is unnoticeable at most frequencies, but when the low note is very low, in the bass region, the cone excursions are large and the variations are slow enough to have an audible effect, especially if the high note is much higher, in the mid or treble range.

At moderate powers the amplitude of the bass cone is insufficient for the doppler effect to be detectable, the pitch changes are too small. But at high power, when the bass cone is really moving, then it can be, and the effect can be quite unpleasant.

So, if the rig is to run at very high power, a three-way

system using a mid-range unit, or a nest of them, will sound better than a two-way with just a tweeter and bass driver.

The disadvantage is the difficulty in getting the crossover circuit right and all the units to match. As shown in Chapter 8, while an approximate design can be produced for a given set of drivers, it often needs to be fine-tuned by trial and error, and some makers employ computers to do the design because of the many variable factors. While this is so with a two-way system, the problem is considerably compounded with a three-way. For this and other reasons, three-way systems have largely gone out of fashion in hi-fi circles.

So, it all comes down to the power; high power needs a three-way, but more moderate power is best with two-way systems.

An amount of beaming occurs with mid-range units as well as tweeters. For large rigs then, a pair set at angles in a suitable enclosure gives a wide coverage. If a mid-range unit is fitted in the same cabinet as the bass unit, it should be mounted with an air-tight box around it to shield it from the large air pressure variations set up by the bass unit.

Monitors

When a group are playing behind a stack, it can be difficult to hear just what the effect is, especially if the audience is noisy. A monitor or 'fold back' loudspeaker is thus necessary to feed sound on stage. This needs to be a full-range unit although extreme bass and treble are not necessary. High power is not essential, and could lead to feedback with the on-stage microphones if the volume is too high.

The choice of cabinet type is therefore not critical. An infinite baffle, or reflex can be used, but the former is the most straightforward as there is no port to worry about. A two-way system consisting of bass unit and tweeter is suitable, but for less complication and an uncoloured result, it is worth considering a twin-cone full-range driver. Altai and McKenzie have suitable models, and there is an 8-inch full-range unit by the manufacturer Volt, which has a good reputation.

A wedge shape is much favoured for the cabinet with the front sloping upward. It can thus be placed on the floor of the stage, and be directed toward the heads of the performers.

A refinement which can be useful is a volume control which enables the level to be adjusted during performance if need be without upsetting the balance of other units that may be operating from the same amplifier. Special high power controls of 30 watts rating are obtainable for the purpose.

Cabaret

Cabaret turns often have to perform in restricted venues and to smaller audiences than groups, so the equipment should reflect this. Loudspeakers can be smaller — and less bulky to transport. If the turn is only vocal, a single 10-inch full-range driver in an open-backed cabinet — that is with an acoustically open back — should serve the purpose well. Two cabinets may be required to cover a wide area if such a situation should arise. High power is not usually necessary.

If the stage is low or non-existent, loudspeaker cabinets placed on the floor will be masked by the front of the audience. There may be no suitable objects on which to stand them, so an essential item of the equipment should be a loudspeaker stand for each unit. These are like a more substantial version of a microphone stand with fittings at the top to secure the loudspeaker, and are collapsible for transportation. A loudspeaker on a stand does not excite bass resonances in the platform which can happen when a loudspeaker unit is standing directly upon it, and so does not produce a bassy, chesty sound, but is clearer and more natural.

Feedback between loudspeaker and microphone can also take place through the flooring from a floor-standing loudspeaker. This is less likely when the loudspeaker is on a stand, especially if the stand has rubber feet. Feedback can and does still take place through air coupling, but the problem is reduced when one possible path is thus eliminated.

If the turn is instrumental, a loudspeaker will have to be chosen that will reproduce the range of the instrument. A higher power amplifier and loudspeaker than is needed for a purely vocal sound would be required. This is because the sounds made by many instruments have large starting transients which could produce distortion in an under-powered system.

In most cases, the best choice would be for an infinite baffle sealed box loudspeaker, unless the instrument has a very low register below around 49 Hz (G_3) in which case a reflex system would be preferred.

Percussion

Percussion instruments have no particular pitch except the tympani or kettle drum. A 30-inch tympani will tune down to 87 Hz, which is F_2, while the lowest pitch of a 23-inch is 116 Hz or B flat$_2$. They are though not usually used for group work, so apart from these and the large bass drum, fundamental percussion sounds do not extend into the bass register. Loudspeakers for reproducing percussion do not therefore need a good bass response.

All percussion instruments produce very large starting transients that die away rapidly. These consist of high frequencies that can extend up to and beyond the range of human hearing; the spectrum of a cymbal clash has been measured up to 25 kHz. It follows that the loudspeaker must have an extended high-frequency response if it is to reproduce the bite and attack of the original. This can be achieved by the use of a tweeter partnered with a mid-range unit. Furthermore, the tweeter should have a wide angle of dispersion because without it most of the audience will miss the effect.

Although the average power of a percussion sound is low because of its rapid decay, the large starting transients require high power to reproduce. The tweeter should thus be adequately rated, and if possible more than one used.

Probably the best arrangement is a 10-inch or 12-inch driver in an open-backed cabinet similar to that for the lead guitar, with two tweeters in a separate tweeter box (Design 10, page 156). Units having the internal crossover will simplify matters.

Chapter 11

CABINET CONSTRUCTION

Having chosen the plan or designed our own system, we can now turn to the actual work of constructing the cabinet. First of all we will take a look at the different types of wood that are available. Plywood can be obtained in many thicknesses and grades. The number of plies vary from 3 to 19, but they are always an odd number to inhibit warping. Grades range from type A, which is guaranteed free from surface defects to WG which is very rough and normally used for packing cases. Type B/BB is preferred for speaker cabinets because one side is first grade, but the other may have plugs. These are inserts glued in to replace knot holes. This side of course goes inside the enclosure.

Another form of wood is blockboard, in which a number of rough blocks are sandwiched between two facing sheets, and laminboard which is similar but contains a larger number of smaller blocks. The latter has better damping properties than conventional plywood, but the edges have to be disguised with veneer unless all outside joints are mitred.

Chipboard is another much favoured material. It is made by compressing resin coated wooden chips between steel plates. Here too there are numerous grades. Single layer chipboard consists of chips of the same size throughout and so has a consistent density. Three-layer chipboard has two outer layers of high density to give a better surface finish with a lower density interior. The multi-layer grade has two outer high density layers and also a high density core with lower density in between. There is also a graded density chipboard in which the density varies gradually throughout its thickness (Fig.27).

The densities are rated by weight and range from 400 to 900 kg/m^3 although some cement loaded grades go up to 1150 kg/m^3. The best for speaker enclosures is a single layer high density type of at least 600 kg/m^3. This is especially so for the front panel where rebated holes may have to be cut for the drivers. Alternatively plywood could

101

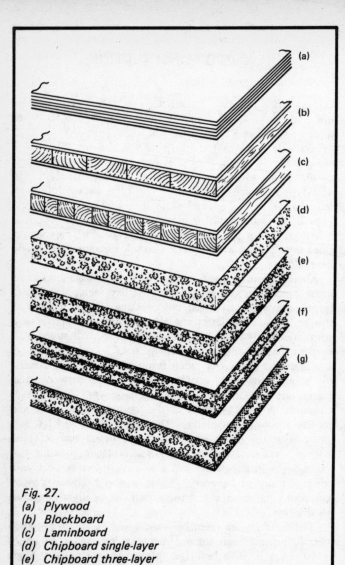

Fig. 27.
(a) Plywood
(b) Blockboard
(c) Laminboard
(d) Chipboard single-layer
(e) Chipboard three-layer
(f) Chipboard multi-layer
(g) Chipboard graded density

be used here. Chipboard is available veneered on one side which solves the finishing problem providing the edges are rebated with care.

Another material gaining in popularity is fibreboard. In this the wood is reduced to fibres which are felted and pressed into sheets with little or no extra resin being added. The bond arises from the felting and the natural adhesion between the fibres. Sheets are tempered into hardboards by impregnating with oil or resin and heat treating.

The density of fibreboard is higher than chipboard ranging from 800 to 1200 kg/m^3, and it also has frictional losses between the fibres which increase its damping factor. It has a smooth finish on one side, and a grainy one on the other. Thickness is limited at present to ½-inch, but medium density fibreboard (MDF) from 640 to 860 kg/m^3 is now available up to 1½-inch thick.

When plywood is used for hi-fi enclosures it has been found that lining with builders' plasterboard has a better effect and is superior to the same thickness of plywood. So a ⅜-inch sheet of plywood bonded to a ⅜-inch sheet of plasterboard is better than a ¾-inch sheet of plywood. Remember to allow for this or any other damping material fixed to the inside surface of the cabinet when working out the dimensions. It is the inside dimensions that matter.

For small to medium sized enclosures, a rather surprising discovery is that thinner wood is best providing it is lined inside with thick bituminous pads. Suitable pads are available from specialist mail-order loudspeaker dealers such as Wilmslow Audio. This arrangement seems to be one of the most effective methods of reducing panel resonances in wooden enclosures. As we saw in an earlier chapter, damping material fixed to the inside surface of the enclosure has no effect on the internal dimensional air resonances because these boundaries are at the nodes of the standing waves and effective damping requires absorbent at the antinodes. However, it is essential to deal with the panel resonances.

For most of the panels, the damping need not extend over the whole inside surface as long as it covers at least 60% of the central area. It may be easier for calculating the internal air volume though, if it does in fact extend to the edges. The inside of the back panel should be fully covered to reduce the reflected wave which otherwise would be reflected back to the drive unit and pass out, delayed, through the cone.

While each of the various types of wood we have described have their features, the overriding one for musicians on the road is that of strength and durability. For this, thick plywood is best.

Driver Access

One major difference affecting construction, between hi-fi loudspeakers and those designed for professional music making, is that of access to the driver. Hi-fi units are usually made as nicely finished pieces of furniture, wood veneered all around and there is no user access to the drive units. Such access of course is rarely, if ever, necessary.

With the professional music loudspeaker access is desirable. Although the drive units are designed for heavy use, they do get a lot of hard work and sometimes abuse. Accidents can easily happen, and the driver can be damaged either physically or due to power overloading. Sometimes distortion arising in the amplifier can damage a loudspeaker driver.

In addition to this, the player may have several drive units that he wants to try out in the same enclosure. Easy replacement is thus an important feature.

The easiest method is to mount the driver from the front, then it can be readily dropped out without disturbing the cabinet panels at all. To make a good job of this, a rebate should be cut surrounding the cut-out hole so that the loudspeaker chassis can be sunk into it. Some may still protrude along with the covering grille, but it gives a shallower front profile and is less likely to suffer damage.

If rebating is beyond the skills or tool complement of the cabinet builder, it is not absolutely necessary and the driver can be mounted against the front panel surface although it will be more vulnerable.

Fitting the driver inside affords greater protection against physical damage but means that a panel must be made detachable if there is to be access. Usually this will be the back panel, although it can also be the front. The important thing with detachable panels is that they must be made airtight. This can be done by screwing with No. 10 screws at least every 6 inches and fitting a gasket, which can take the form of self-adhesive foam plastic draught excluder strip. Sealing is only necessary with infinite baffle or reflex cabinets. Open-backed units need not be sealed although the backs should be firmly screwed to prevent vibration.

Securing the Driver

Drivers should not be fitted with woodscrews because these can work loose with the large vibrations to which they are subject. This is not so much due to the screw turning, but compression of the threads it has cut in the wood. Nuts and bolts are less likely to work loose, especially if a shake-proof washer is put under the nut. Bolt heads can be recessed into the front panel and the nut applied to retain the loudspeaker chassis.

The snag with ordinary nuts and bolts is that the bolt can turn as the nut is tightened. A better idea is to use a clamp kit made for the purpose. This consists of a set of bolts and clamps, and round threaded barrels each with a flange and anchoring pin. A hole is drilled that is big enough to receive the barrel, which is applied from the outside. It is prevented from being drawn fully into the hole by the flange, and the pins pierce the wood thereby preventing the flange and barrel from rotating (Fig.28).

The hole in the clamp is not round but a slot, so that the position can be adjusted as required. This makes positioning the bolt holes less critical.

Clamps can be used on the outside to secure front mounted drivers, in which case the bolt heads will also be on the outside. The clamps can then also hold the covering grille.

In theory, any material generally used for domestic loud-speakers including fabric or Tygan, could be used to cover the driver aperture. But the degree of protection needed for 'on the road' use is much greater. The effect of some long narrow object such as a microphone stand accidentally spearing a cloth-covered loudspeaker aperture, can well be imagined. Steel grilles are much safer, and can be obtained in all the standard loudspeaker sizes from 5 to 18 inches in diameter.

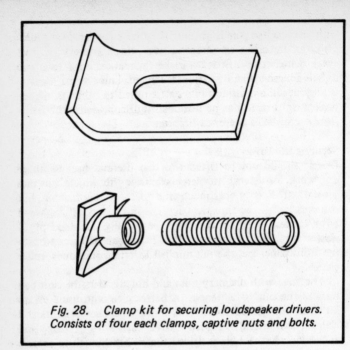

Fig. 28. Clamp kit for securing loudspeaker drivers. Consists of four each clamps, captive nuts and bolts.

Cutting

Cutting the wood, which should be well supported and marked, is easiest done with a power circular saw having fine teeth. Try to make the cut all in one go, because stopping and restarting can produce a step in the edge of the wood. One problem is that sawdust can settle on the work ahead of the saw and obscure the mark, so you have to stop to clear it. A method of countering this is to have an assistant with a vacuum cleaner hose fitted with a crevice device to suck away the sawdust as it forms. This will also keep your workshop (kitchen, spare room, dining room) cleaner and so result in less aggro to the distaff side of the family.

Note that cuts along the grain are clean but those across it often result in splintering to the underside of the work. So ensure that you cut from the outside surface so that any splintered edges will be inside.

The loudspeaker aperture and other cut-outs must be done with a fretsaw attachment to the power unit. First drill a hole within the cut-out area near the marked edge, then insert the saw and swing out at an angle to follow the mark around. A stop will almost certainly be required to make a 360° cut, probably more than one, but any discontinuities caused by these can be sanded down afterward. The loudspeaker cuts will be concealed by the grille so do not need to be perfect.

A golden rule with the use of all power tools is to run the cable around you to the rear so that there is no possibility of it falling across the work. Many have overlooked this possibility with tragic consequences.

Jointing

There are many ways of making a joint. Skilled carpenters will prefer to use rebate, dovetail, tongue and groove, mitres, or other fancy jointing. However, acoustically they have no advantage over the simple butt joint, providing the joints are flat along their whole length, and they are glued and screwed at no more than 6-inch (150mm) intervals. All must be absolutely airtight.

Evo-Stik wood glue is recommended although other makes would probably be just as satisfactory. Evo-Stik comes in a convenient plastic container with a spout which enables it to be easily applied to the work without messy brushes or applicators. A small woodscrew screwed in the end of the spout after use, will keep the glue usable for months. It is also very strong, and sets hard and solid. It thus fills in any cracks and crevices in the wood, so ensuring an airtight joint.

Square-section battens should be glued at the back of each joint to reinforce it, and along the back edges to help support the rear panel, but this should be screwed to the actual sides, not to the battens.

Connections

The loudspeaker wires should be soldered to the drivers and to the crossover unit if any. They can then be brought out to a connector at the back. There are various types of connectors that can be used, the most common being the ¼-inch jack socket, the sprung compression terminal, and the XLR socket.

The jack socket is cheap, easy to connect, and affords a good contact with the plug. As the plug is a straightforward push-in, it has the advantage that it will pull out without damage should someone trip over the wire.

However, many jack plugs at present on the market have been found to give trouble. The rivets which hold the terminal pieces to the body and centre contact post often make poor contact although they appear to be tight. Also the barrel and tip contacts are often chrome plated which looks fine, but does not always give good electrical contact. Most of these are Oriental in origin, but components made by reputable British manufacturers rarely suffer from these problems. So, if using jack plugs and sockets make sure you get reputable British made ones, they may be more expensive but they are well worth it.

Sprung terminal posts are another option. With these, a press button is held down and the bare wire is inserted in a hole in the terminal. Releasing the button causes the wire to be gripped by a sprung contact. These seem quite convenient and need no plugs on the wire ends, but are not without their drawbacks.

With stranded cables, an odd strand can easily escape from the bunch — and often does. If this happens to touch a free strand from the other cable, there will be a short-circuit across the amplifier and a likely burn out. Apart from this possibility, before actually connecting into the loudspeaker you have a lead with bare ends, which could result in disaster if they should touch when the amplifier is on. Then it is not always easy to find the holes in the terminal with the cable when struggling at the bottom-end of a large cabinet in poor light.

The third option is the XLR connector. These make good solid contact, and lock into position so that they cannot be accidentally pulled out. This though can be a disadvantage if someone trips over the wire, as then the cable is likely to be torn out leaving the connector still in place in the socket. With these connectors a quick 'first aid' job to get things going again is just not possible.

Even so, and though the XLR is the most expensive of the trio, it seems the best option. Accidents of the above nature can be minimised by having some surplus cable coiled neatly behind the loudspeaker. Then if anyone does inadvertently yank it, the strain will be taken up by the spare and not pull at the connector. A related tip here: most breakdowns are caused by faulty cables, whether in the loudspeaker circuit, microphones or instruments. So when on the road always carry a complete set of spares.

Dishes are available for mounting the connectors. These are recessed panels with flanges, and need cut-outs on the back panel to accommodate them. They are drilled ready for fixing screws and usually have two socket holes. The second socket is connected in parallel with the first and enables another loudspeaker to be connected.

Finishing

If desired, the edges, particularly the front edges, can be rounded off with a file and finished with sandpaper. This gives a good appearance but also has the practical advantage of being less prone to damage. Corners and edges always seem to suffer from the hard knocks which surely come.

An alternative is to fit edging and corner pieces. Matching edging and corners are available in tough plastic which can be glued and nailed in place. This gives a pleasing effect and covers any splintering or other defects in cutting the edges. If any should be damaged later, they can always be replaced. Bright metal corners are also available.

Here is a good tip for using nails, especially near corners and edges. There is always a danger of the wood splitting, but this possibility can be greatly reduced if the nail is first blunted by holding it upright on a solid base and tapping the point with a hammer, before driving into the wood.

The reason why wood splits is that a sharp nail acts as a wedge, pushing its way between the wood fibres and forcing them apart. A blunt nail behaves as a punch, compressing the wood ahead of it as it is driven in. It takes more energy to drive it home, but it is far less likely to cause a split.

Another tip to make any nailed joint more secure and reduce the possibility of the nails pulling out under stress, is skew nailing. Instead of driving each nail straight in, alternate ones are driven at a slight and opposite angle to the previous one. Moderate stress from any angle cannot pull the joint apart because at least some of the nails will be at a different angle from that of the pull. While skew nailing is not as strong as using screws, it is stronger than straight nailing, and so can be used for moderate loads. The only disadvantage is that the nail heads are at an angle, but they can be hammered flat or can be countersunk and puttied over.

Handles are an essential item as there will usually be much carrying to do. Straps on the top may be adequate for the smaller cabinet, but most will require heavy-duty handles at each side. Like the connecting terminals these should be recessed. Any protruding parts are likely to suffer when in transit and could cause damage to other items of equipment. Furthermore much packing space can be wasted because of surface mounted pieces. Handles for heavy cabinets should be fitted above the centre of gravity so that the unit does not tend to topple over when being carried, yet at a height which makes it easy to walk while holding the cabinet well clear of the ground.

Rubber feet are a useful addition as these can reduce feedback through the stage, and prevent slipping during transit. Very heavy units can be fitted with castors which are also available for the purpose. These would greatly help in transporting from vehicle to venue, but could create a problem when in transit. Units with castors are best transported face downward with their castors off the floor.

The safest way to transport the equipment is to line the floor of the vehicle with foam plastic of at least 2 inches (50 mm) thickness. Tall cabinets whether with castors or not can then be laid face downward on it and other items placed so as to make the maximum use of the available space. The foam exerts a firm grip which greatly inhibits sliding about even when negotiating sharp corners.

After the cut-outs for handles and connections are made but before actually fitting them and the corner and edge pieces if used, the woodwork itself must be given a suitable finish. Plastic, vinyl, fabric and wood veneer are all finishes that are used for domestic hi-fi cabinets, but are rather too fragile for road work. If damaged any of these are not easy to repair without spoiling the whole appearance.

The most practical finish is paint, which can always be touched up if required. First, the wood needs to be sanded down to give a reasonably good surface and remove obvious blemishes. Then it must be primed. If this is omitted, the paint will likely soak into the wood and dry patchily.

Choice of colour is of course optional, but black is serviceable and can always be embellished with gold or silver lettering or motifs. Matt paints shows up faults less than gloss and is more serviceable, but an option worth considering is Hammerite which dries to a crackle finish. This effectively disguises blemishes in the wood and also looks quite attractive.

After the paint has dried, it might need two coats or more, then the handles, connector dish, corners and any other appendage can be fitted. It is important to remember that anything mounted in a cut-out must be just as airtight as the joints. So ensure that there are no unfilled holes. Also, spread a little sealing compound around under the edge of the flange before screwing it down tight. Some constructors go to great lengths to render all their wood joints airtight, but then forget the cut-outs.

Chapter 12

IMPEDANCE MATCHING

There are few problems in matching the impedances of amplifiers and loudspeakers as far as musical instruments are concerned, but we should know what is involved so that errors can be avoided.

For optimum transference of power between amplifier and loudspeaker, the rated output impedance of the amplifier must equal that of the loudspeaker. If the loudspeaker impedance is greater than that of the amplifier, maximum power will not be achieved, but no harm will be done. The important thing is that the combined impedance of all loudspeakers connected to any amplifier never falls below its rated impedance.

Should this happen, excessive current will flow in the amplifier circuits which could burn out the output transistors. Above all else, short-circuits across the loudspeaker cable while the amplifier is operating must be avoided, as this could cause instant destruction of the transistors. As pointed out in an earlier chapter, care should be taken with all loudspeaker connections, and stray whiskers of wire should be avoided for this reason.

Many amplifiers have protection circuits that shut them down in the event of excessive current flowing. While this affords a degree of protection, it is not wise to rely on it, and it could be most inconvenient if it happened in the middle of a performance.

Most large amplifiers have an output impedance of four ohms, while smaller ones sometimes are rated at eight ohms. This sets the minimum limit below which the loudspeaker impedance cannot be allowed to fall. Most drivers have an impedance of eight ohms which means that two connected in parallel will have a combined impedance of four ohms and thus fully load the amplifier.

The formula for calculating loudspeaker impedance in parallel is:

$$Z = \frac{z_1 \times z_2}{z_1 + z_2}$$

or

$$\frac{1}{Z} = \frac{1}{z_1} + \frac{1}{z_2} + \frac{1}{z_3} + \dots$$

The second one must be used when there are more than two impedances.

A question may arise as to the impedance of a multi-driver loudspeaker, that is one with tweeter and mid-range unit as well as the bass. It may seem that with these connected in parallel via the crossover circuit, the impedance would be very low.

While the impedance of such a loudspeaker is complex, it will not in most cases stray much below the nominal rated eight ohms if at all. One reason is that the crossover circuit itself has an impedance which is in series with the drivers. Also, the drivers will not all be working at full power at the same time, and so will not all be loading the amplifier simultaneously. When a high note is being played for example, the bass driver circuit presents a high impedance to the amplifier.

Actually, even a single driver does not present the rated eight ohms at all frequencies, the impedance rises with frequency within its range due to the inductance of the loudspeaker coil.

Multiple Loudspeakers
So, even for multi-driver loudspeakers, a pair can safely be connected to a four-ohm output. But what if more loudspeakers are required? There are some 16-ohm drivers, of which four could be connected in parallel, but these should not be used if only single loudspeaker systems are intended, as most of the amplifier's power would not then be realized. Usually it is best to stick to the standard eight ohms unless a multi-unit set-up from the same amplifier is intended for all occasions

114

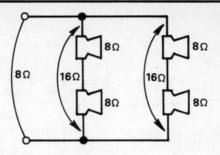

Fig. 29. Four loudspeakers in series-parallel. Impedance of each series pair is 16 Ω, and two pairs in parallel bring the total to 8 Ω, the same as for a single unit.

To operate four eight-ohm loudspeakers from a four-ohm output, requires the use of a series-parallel arrangement. The configuration is shown in Figure 29. It will be seen that there are two pairs, each unit is connected in series with another, then each pair is connected in parallel to the other pair.

The impedance of such an arrangement is eight ohms, the same as for a single unit. This is a useful rule to remember, a four-way series-parallel circuit will always have the same impedance as that of a single unit providing all units have the same impedance.

In theory, another loudspeaker could be connected across the amplifier as its eight ohms and that of the series-parallel combination would bring the total to four ohms, just right for the amplifier. However, there would be a disproportionate power distribution between them. Half the power would go to the extra loudspeaker, and the other half would be shared between the four, which would thus get one-eighth of the power each.

This could be put to good use such as having a large high-powered loudspeaker in centre stage wired across the amplifier direct, and another four smaller ones in series parallel, two at each end of the platform to fill in the sides.

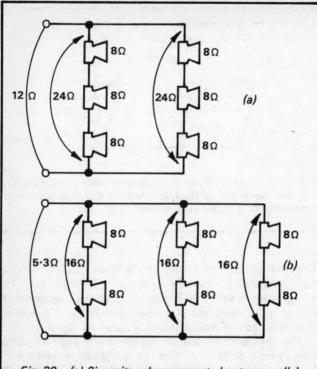

Fig. 30. (a) Six units, when connected as two parallel groups of series threes, have a total impedance of 12 Ω. (b) When connected as three groups of series pairs the impedance is 5.3 Ω.

It is perhaps unlikely that six loudspeakers would be required to run from the same amplifier, but if so, a series parallel arrangement can be utilized. There are two possible combinations. One has two groups of three in which the three units in each group are in series, and the two groups are connected in parallel. The impedance in this case is 12 ohms.

The second arrangement has three pairs of units in which the units of each pair are connected in series, and the three pairs then connected in parallel. This produces an impedance

116

of 5.3 ohms.

It can be seen that the second one gives better power transfer from the amplifier (Fig.30).

Connections

When using four units in series-parallel, complications are avoided during the setting up if all connections are made inside the loudspeakers so that all that needs to be done is to plug the leads in the right places.

Most terminal dishes have space for two connecting sockets. If three-pin XLR connectors are used they can be wired as shown in Figure 31. The internal connection circuits have been designed so that any external lead can be used to link any two speakers. This cuts down the possibility of error when connecting up, and saves time.

Three cores are needed, so a heavy gauge mains cable will serve the purpose. Twin cable can be used between the amplifier and first loudspeaker. When making up each lead the central third pins are connected together, but the left pin of one plug goes to the right of the other as can be seen from the diagram. The second socket of loudspeaker No. 4 is not used so one need not be fitted, in which case the hole in the dish will have to be blanked off.

Note that the internal connections to the drivers in Nos. 3 and 4 are opposite to those in 1 and 2. This is necessary to make all the leads the same and preserve phase, more of which later.

The loudspeakers must be connected in the sequence shown, so they should be numbered on the back, and the 'in' and 'out' sockets distinguished. If only two units are required for a smaller venue, either Nos. 1 and 2, or 3 and 4 can be used. If only one is needed either No. 2 or 4 are the ones to use. The two pairs could be fed from two separate amps if desired, connecting one amp to No. 1 and the other to No. 3, omitting the link between 2 and 3. The system is thus very versatile.

Phasing

When connecting drivers internally or loudspeaker units, it is essential to ensure that they are all in phase. That is, that all

117

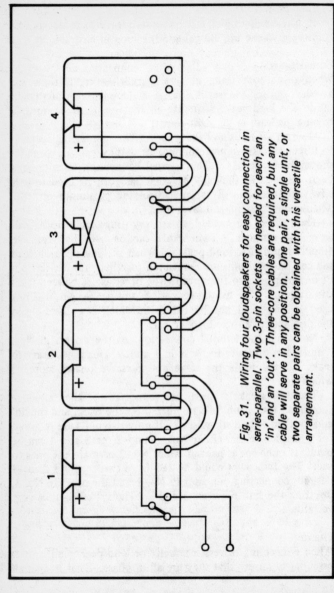

Fig. 31. Wiring four loudspeakers for easy connection in series-parallel. Two 3-pin sockets are needed for each, an 'in' and an 'out'. Three-core cables are required, but any cable will serve in any position. One pair, a single unit, or two separate pairs can be obtained with this versatile arrangement.

cones are moving in the same direction at the same time. If not, they will cancel instead of reinforce each other. The resulting sound will be thin and lacking in bass, and at some point between them may almost disappear.

Correct phasing is achieved by connecting all the drivers the same way. One terminal is usually marked in some way, often with a red spot. It is termed the positive, not that any d.c. potential is normally involved, but this the terminal which, if a d.c. positive potential was applied would produce a forward movement of the cone.

When connecting in parallel, all these terminals should be connected together. When in series, the positive or marked terminal of one speaker goes to the negative or unmarked terminal of the other. In a series-parallel arrangement, those in parallel are connected with positives together, then these groups are connected with their positives to the negatives of the next group as shown in Figure 32.

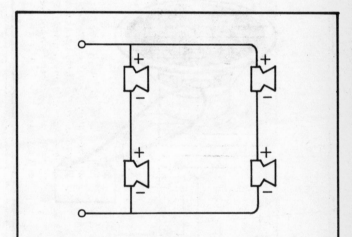

Fig. 32. Phase must be observed when connecting drivers. In a series-parallel arrangement, parallel groups must be connected with all positives together, but with series sections positives are connected to the next negative.

119

In the case of an unmarked driver, its polarity can be easily determined by using a dry battery with terminals (not a car battery which could damage the coil). Connect the negative terminal of the battery to one of the terminals of the driver and fit a wire to the positive. Touch this wire to the other driver terminal and observe the direction of the cone movement. If it is forward, the touched terminal is the positive, if backward, the other is positive. Mark accordingly.

If the motion of the cone is too small to see, gently place a finger at the centre of the cone. When the wire is contacted it should be possible to feel the direction of movement (Fig. 33).

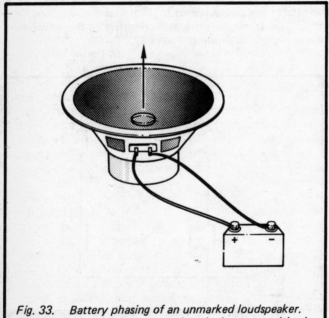

Fig. 33. Battery phasing of an unmarked loudspeaker. The terminal which is connected to the battery positive is the '+' or red spot when the cone moves upward. Contact to battery should be only momentary.

Chapter 13

CABINET DESIGNS

From the previous chapters it should be possible to design a sealed enclosure for any particular driver providing the Thiele-Small parameters are known. These are usually available from most British manufacturers, but rarely from Oriental ones. The lesson is obvious. Although a reflex enclosure is tricky to design, it can be attempted by a straightforward calculation of the enclosure volume, then using different lengths of pipe while measuring the dips in current through the driver, to determine the correct pipe length. This process was described in Chapter 5.

In general, reflex enclosures should be used for deep bass and full range loudspeakers, but sealed box cabinets for everything else except the lead guitar which can be used with open-backed units.

We now describe and illustrate ten designs provided by Celestion. These were designed for their own drivers, but could be used with other makes if the parameters are similar. One point to be noted is that loudspeaker manufacturers now regularly change their models. Often the changes are minor and frequently only cosmetic, but as the new models appear with different model numbers they cannot easily be identified with the ones they replace.

Because of this, Celestion no longer publish driver model numbers for specified designs, from fear of them being discontinued before the design is built! Not a very helpful situation, but they will reply to individual enquiries and suggest models from their current range for any particular enclosure, should the stated one not be available.

With each design we have suggested a driver which has the nearest parameters to those required, from the range current at the time of printing. In some cases the design was for an older model, so we have had to modify their measurements to suit the driver now available.

The calculated lower frequency range as described by the f_3 limit is given in Hz along with its musical key. The actual response may be a little different from that calculated but it serves to give some idea of the range. In each case the response goes below the f_3 point, falling off at the rate of about 12 dB per octave for sealed enclosures and 24 dB per octave for reflex ones.

The upper response is also given in frequency but not in the musical key. This is because a much higher response than the highest note to be produced is needed to generate the harmonics and overtones. Most drivers, even the large bass ones, will produce the fundamentals of high treble notes, but not their harmonics.

Design 1 - General Purpose Bass (Fig.34)

This is a reflex enclosure for bass instruments, or for the bass end of keyboard instruments with a separate treble unit. Dimensions are given for each of four different cone sizes, 10-, 12-, 15- and 18-inch. There are also three options for each cone size, each producing the same internal volume but wih different shapes.

The larger the cone the lower the bass response, although it is only the 18-inch driver that shows an appreciable difference. However, its limited treble response restricts it to either a low bass instrument or use with a separate treble unit.

Construction is easy, using ¾-inch (18 mm) ply. All joints are reinforced inside with 20 mm or 30 mm square batten, as are all the projects here described.

Cone Size	Cabinet Volume	Bass f_3	Musical Note	Treble	Driver
10-inch	30 L	74 Hz	D_2	6.0 kHz	G10T 75 CE
12-inch	50 L	71 Hz	D_2	4.5 kHz	S12 150 CE
15-inch	100 L	69 Hz	$C\#_2$	5.0 kHz	S15 250 CE
18-inch	150 L	40 Hz	E_3	3.0 kHz	B18 300

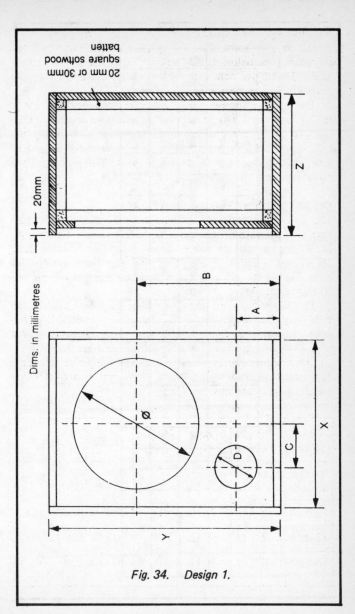

20mm or 30mm square softwood batten

20mm

Dims. in millimetres

Fig. 34. Design 1.

123

SPEAKER SIZE	VOL. (Litres)	OPTION 1						OPTION 2						OPTION 3								Port Length
		X	Y	Z	A	B	C	X	Y	Z	A	B	C	X	Y	Z	A	B	C	D	Ø	
10"	30	315	540	245	120	360	0	.	.	.	.	.	.	286	477	294	80	290	0	76	230	.
12"	50	374	634	280	130	411	0	369	497	350	85	300	100	339	558	338	90	335	0	102	283	62
15"	100	470	790	338	140	482	0	464	616	427	110	380	130	427	695	412	120	420	0	152	355	159
18"	150	539	898	380	160	560	0	530	700	480	120	420	150	489	790	463	140	490	0	152	420	117

Fig. 34. Design 1.

124

Design 2 - Vocal Full-range (Fig.35)

This loudspeaker is a sealed box type with an h.f. unit. The bass driver is the 12-inch S12 150 CE, and the treble unit, the HF50 X. Celestion's original design was for another, now obsolete driver, and has been modified to reduce the volume from 45 to 36 L to give the optimum Q for the available unit.

The h.f. unit is obtainable with or without the suffix X. Those with the suffix have a built-in crossover which filters at 3 kHz. It saves complication if one of these is used as it can then be connected straight across the bass unit. Do not connect an HF50 without the X suffix across the bass driver, these MUST have a separate crossover circuit.

Frequency response is from 117 Hz (B flat$_2$) to 16 kHz. The bass is limited but perfectly adequate for vocal work or even a lead guitar, although the response is rather smooth for that, lacking the bite that most electronic guitar players prefer. It would be very suitable though, for amplifying an acoustic guitar or other treble acoustic instrument.

Its compact size makes it ideal for cabaret work where space may be restricted. It is particularly effective on a tall stand.

Construction is easy with ¾-inch (18 mm) plywood. The hole for the bass driver is shown rebated, but this is not essential, the driver can be fitted externally without it. When fitted internally, rebating is not required.

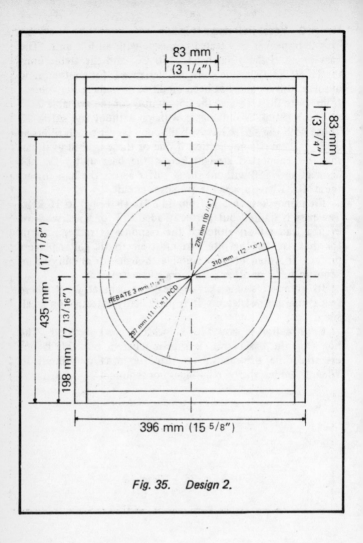

83 mm
(3 1/4")

83 mm
(3 1/4")

276 mm (10 7/8")

310 mm (12 1/8")

REBATE 3 mm (1/8")

297 mm (11 11/16") PCD

435 mm (17 1/8")

198 mm (7 13/16")

396 mm (15 5/8")

Fig. 35.   Design 2.

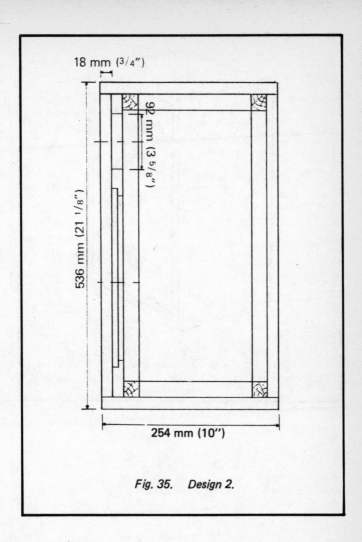

18 mm (³/₄")

92 mm (3 ⁵/₈")

536 mm (21 ¹/₈")

254 mm (10")

Fig. 35.   Design 2.

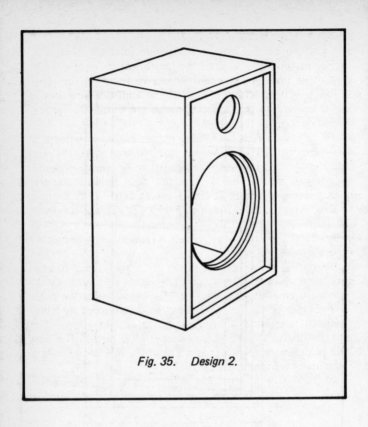

Fig. 35.   Design 2.

Design 3 - Stage Monitor (Fig.36)

The purpose of this unit is to provide foldback, that is to enable performers to hear the performance clearly from behind the main stacks. It is shaped to stand on the floor at low height so as not to restrict the audience view but is angled upward so that the performers are within the vertical dispersion angle of the h.f. unit.

To achieve a reasonable bass response a reflex system is used, although extreme bass is not required. At low frequencies most loudspeaker propagation is omnidirectional, so low bass will be heard from the main stacks. The frequency response is from 71 Hz (D_2) to 16 kHz.

Bass driver is the 12-inch S12 150 CE and the h.f. unit, the HF50 X. The suffix X denotes that it has a built-in crossover so that no further circuit is required; it is connected in parallel with the bass unit.

Volume of the cabinet is 60 L. It is fairly easy to construct from ¾-inch (18 mm) ply, although some pieces have to be cut on an angle. This can be done by adjusting the angle of a circular power saw, but is not so easy if sawn by hand. Accuracy is essential to achieve strong airtight joints. The pipe length for this driver is 4 inches (100 mm). The bass hole is shown rebated, but is not essential and not necessary if the driver is fitted internally.

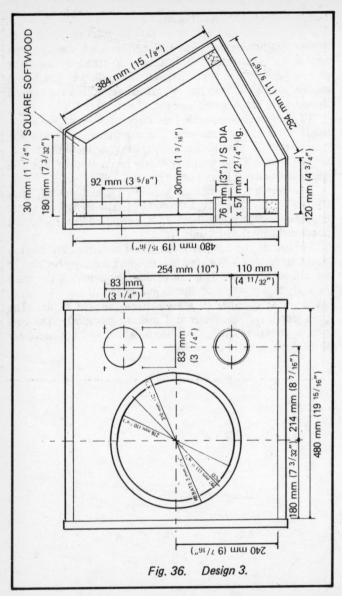

Fig. 36. Design 3.

130

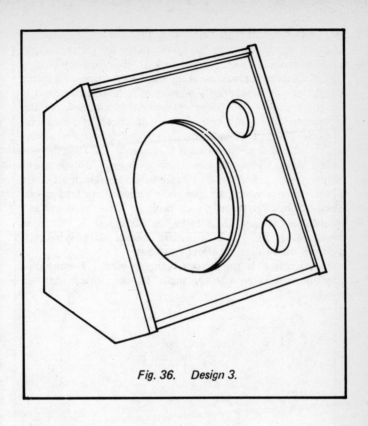

Fig. 36. Design 3.

Design 4 - Lead/Rhythm Guitar (Fig.37)

There is an option with this loudspeaker for either a single 12-inch driver or two 10-inch units. It is an open-backed cabinet although some covering should be fitted to protect the driver. A panel with a number of holes drilled over it is recommended. Being open-backed it is untuned, so the volume and size is not critical nor is the choice of drive units.

Both 10- and 12-inch drivers go well below the lowest note of the lead guitar which is G, however, the 10-inch units have a higher treble response which gives them a brighter and crisper tone. Celestion do a range of three 10-inch and nine 12-inch drivers which are especially designed for lead guitar. They all have paper edges to promote cone break-up and resonances that give the bite to the guitar sound. All these drivers have their own distinctive sound. If possible, try different ones to get the effect you want.

Construction is quite easy, using ½-inch (15 mm) ply. Care must be taken with the angled joints to ensure they are strong.

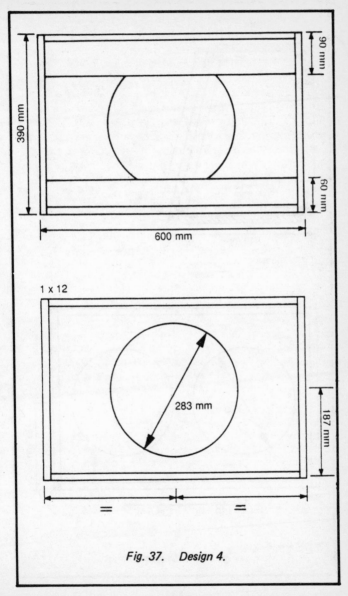

90 mm

390 mm

60 mm

600 mm

1 x 12

283 mm

187 mm

=   =

Fig. 37.   Design 4.

133

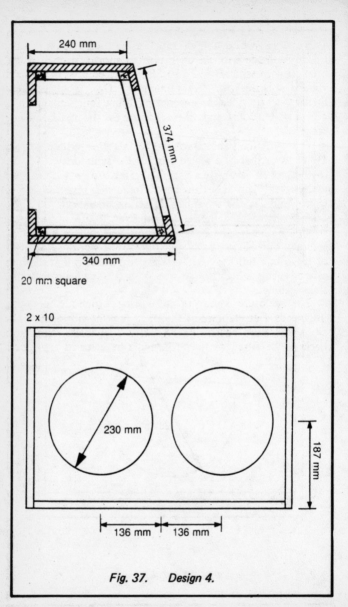

240 mm

374 mm

340 mm

20 mm square

2 x 10

230 mm

187 mm

136 mm   136 mm

Fig. 37.   Design 4.

134

Design 5 - 4 × 12 Bass (Fig.38)

This is a large bass unit of 150 L using four 12-inch drivers. It can be made with an open port as shown, or as a sealed box. If used with an S12 150 CE as a sealed box, the cabinet volume is correct for the optimum 0.7 Q_{tc}. The calculated f_3 for a single driver is lowered by using four units so it is not possible to arrive at an exact figure for the bass frequency range.

The optimum cabinet volume for a reflex system is from 1½ to twice that of a sealed box for the same driver. So, the cabinet, when used with a port as a reflex system, is somewhat undersized. This raises the lower frequency response and so rather nullifies the advantage of reflex operation. A single 18-inch driver used in the Design 1 enclosure of the same volume optimizes the cabinet volume and gives a lower bass response but will not have quite the crispness or the sensitivity of the four 12-inch units. A particular feature is that the four drivers enable a high power of 600 watts to be handled with a single cabinet.

The enclosure is easy to make using ¾-inch (18 mm) ply, but needs a cross brace as shown to prevent vibration of the front and back panels. This does not enable a detachable back to be fitted as the brace must be screwed and glued.

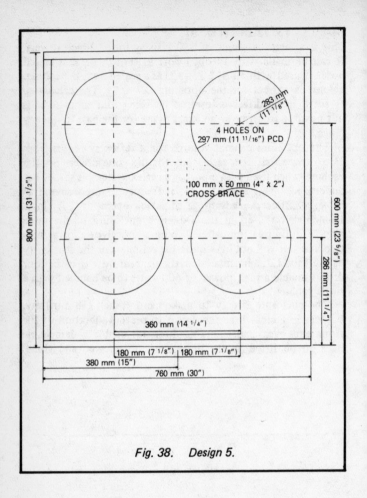

Fig. 38. Design 5.

136

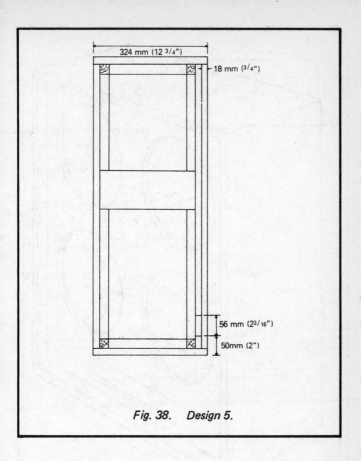

Fig. 38.   Design 5.

137

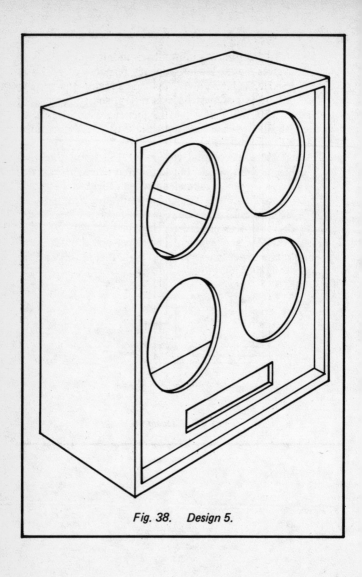

Fig. 38.   *Design 5.*

138

Design 6 - 3-Way Full-range (Fig.39)

For keyboard instruments or foldback monitoring on a large stage, this gives a wide range frequency response of 64 Hz f_3 (C_2) to 16 kHz, at high power. As it is a sealed box system, the bass roll-off is not as steep as a reflex, and so the output is sustained to a well below that frequency. The drivers used are the B18 300 18-inch bass unit; the G10 75 CE mid-range; and two HF 50 treble units.

The enclosure has a total volume of 153 L but there is a 16 L sealed box within, to house the mid-range driver. This box as well as the main cabinet must be airtight and strongly jointed. Construction is straightforward, the material used being ¾-inch (18 mm) plywood.

A three-way crossover network must be used with crossover points at 600 Hz and 3 kHz. The upper one should not be varied, but the lower is less critical. Note that in this case the h.f. units should not have the X suffix.

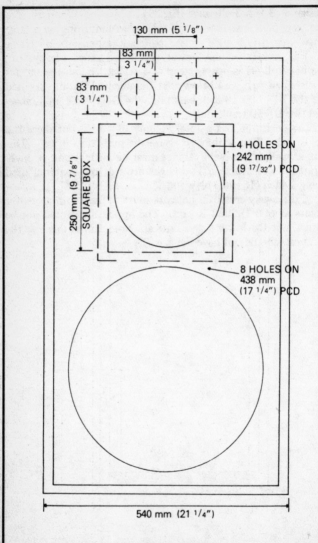

130 mm (5 1/8")

83 mm
3 1/4"

83 mm
(3 1/4")

4 HOLES ON
242 mm
(9 17/32") PCD

250 mm (9 7/8")

SQUARE BOX

8 HOLES ON
438 mm
(17 1/4") PCD

540 mm (21 1/4")

Fig. 39.   Design 6.

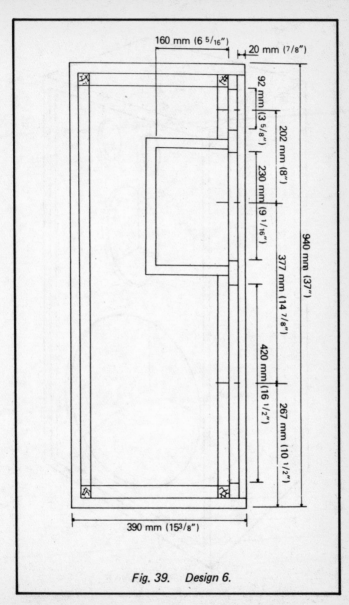

160 mm (6 5/16") 20 mm (7/8")

92 mm (3 5/8")
202 mm (8")
230 mm (9 1/16")
377 mm (14 7/8")
420 mm (16 1/2")
267 mm (10 1/2")
940 mm (37")

390 mm (15 3/8")

Fig. 39.   Design 6.

141

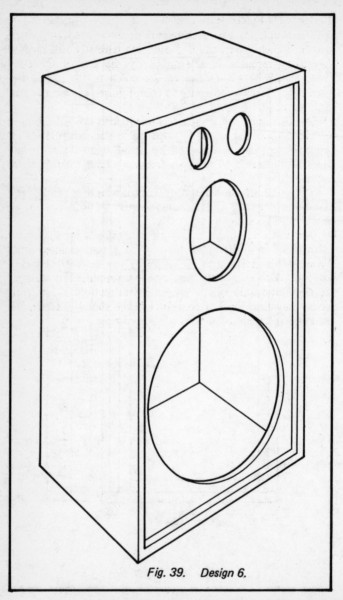

Fig. 39.   Design 6.

Design 7 - W-Folded Horn (Fig.40)

This is a unit for bass instruments or disco bass end, which uses a 15-inch driver, the B15 300. As with all horns the low frequency response is determined by the size of the flare which needs to be massive to get down to the lowest frequencies. Horns are therefore a compromise between size and bass response.

In this design the response is maintained down to around 70 Hz (D_2), but it begins to slope off at about 110 Hz (A_2). Improvement can be obtained by fitting 'barn doors' to the sides as illustrated. The upper frequency limit for this driver is 3 kHz.

There is quite an amount of work involved as can be seen from the diagram, and the angles must be accurate, for all joints must be airtight.

The main advantage is that the system will produce more than twice as much sound for a given output as most other types. This means that the amplifier can be half the power or less. However, with high powered amplifiers now being readily obtainable this is less of an attraction. Also being somewhat directional, it concentrates the sound in front, and so projects it well to the back of the audience.

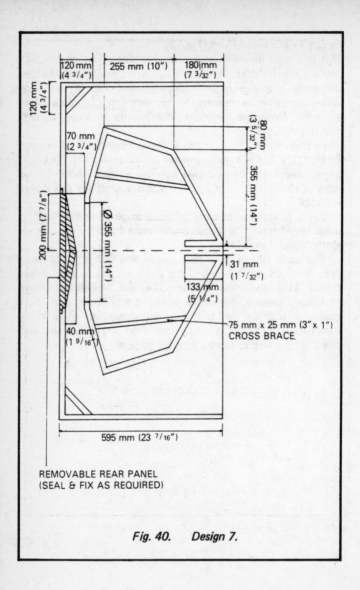

120 mm (4 3/4")

255 mm (10")

180 mm (7 3/32")

120 mm (4 3/4")

70 mm (2 3/4")

80 mm (3 5/32")

355 mm (14")

200 mm (7 7/8")

Ø 355 mm (14")

31 mm (1 7/32")

133 mm (5 1/4")

75 mm x 25 mm (3" x 1") CROSS BRACE

40 mm (1 9/16")

595 mm (23 7/16")

REMOVABLE REAR PANEL
(SEAL & FIX AS REQUIRED)

Fig. 40. Design 7.

144

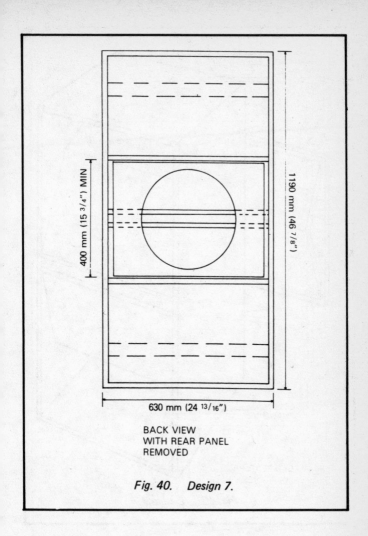

400 mm (15 3/4" MIN

1190 mm (46 7/8")

630 mm (24 13/16")

BACK VIEW
WITH REAR PANEL
REMOVED

Fig. 40. Design 7.

145

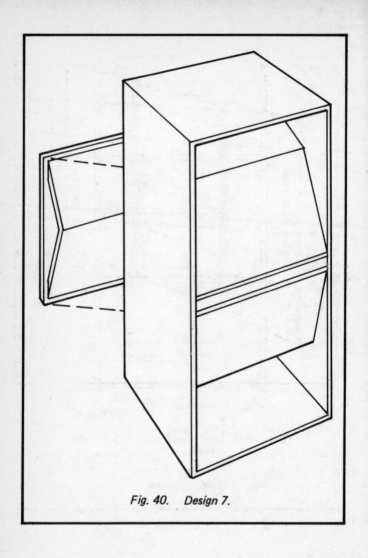

Fig. 40.   Design 7.

146

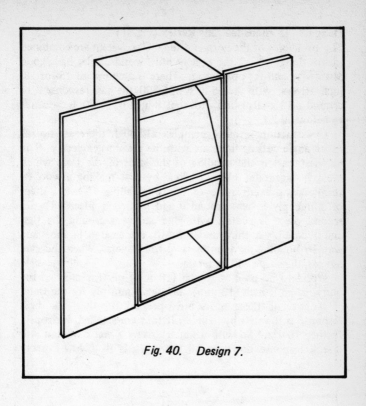

Fig. 40. Design 7.

Design 8 - Horn-loaded Bass Reflex (Fig.41)

The principles of the horn and the reflex system are combined in this design to get the best of both worlds, good bass, good sensitivity and far projection. There is a choice of 15- or 18-inch drivers. With the 15-inch B15 300, the bass response is to around 60 Hz (B_3), and with the 18-inch B18 400, is descends to below 50 Hz.

Construction is quite complex although there are not as many angle cuts as there are with the previous enclosure. The trickiest part is the bending of the sides of the flare which must be accurate. This is done by first making a wooden form having a curvature of 650 mm radius. Next, a sheet of 3 mm ply is bent around it and secured in place. Then a second piece is coated with glue and bent around the first and secured. A third and a fourth are treated in the same way so building up a laminate of four layers. When the glue has set, the shape will be retained.

Wood to be used is ¾-inch (18 mm) ply for most of the body, some ½-inch (12 mm), and the 3 mm ply for the flare.

If two of these units are operated together, the bass response is lowered by 10 Hz. If four are stacked, it drops a further 10 Hz. So with 18-inch drivers a stack of four will give a response down to 30 Hz which is B_3 below bottom C.

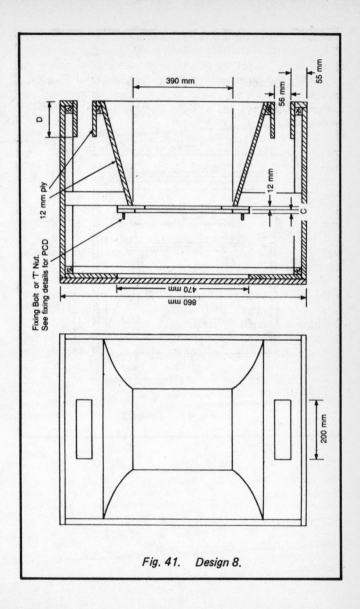

Fig. 41. Design 8.

149

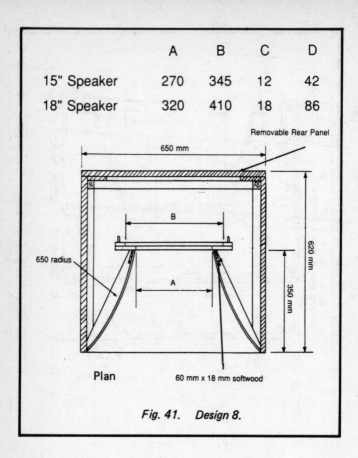

	A	B	C	D
15" Speaker	270	345	12	42
18" Speaker	320	410	18	86

Removable Rear Panel

650 mm

B

650 radius

A

620 mm

350 mm

Plan

60 mm x 18 mm softwood

Fig. 41. Design 8.

150

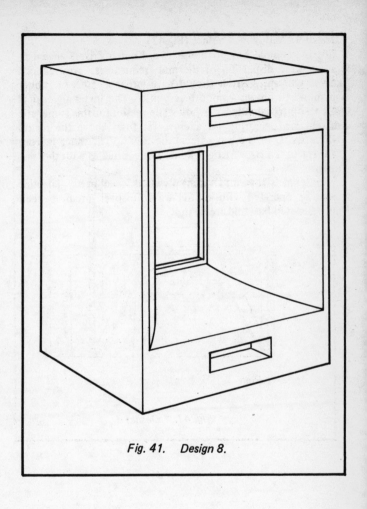

Fig. 41.   Design 8.

Design 9 - Mid-range Cabinet (Fig.42)

This is a simple box to house two 12-inch drivers angled to give a wide dispersion of the mid frequencies. Any 12-inch driver will suit, but it should have either a cloth or rubber surround to obtain a smooth response. The angles are critical but the internal volume is not. The reason for this is that the drivers are operating via a crossover filter above the region where the Q of the box affects the result. The range is from 200 Hz to 2 kHz. Airtight joints are required as with the bass units.

Material is ¾-inch (18 mm) plywood for all parts. The unit must be operated with a three-way crossover circuit to feed an associated bass and treble unit.

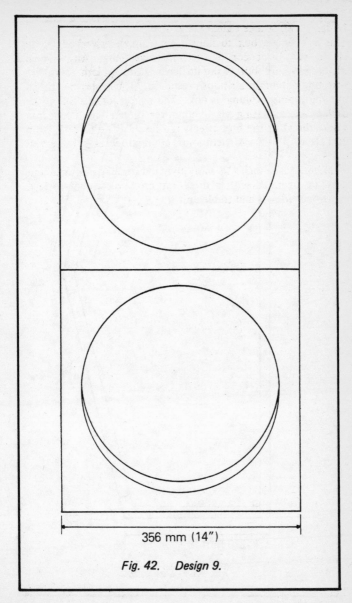

356 mm (14")

Fig. 42.   Design 9.

153

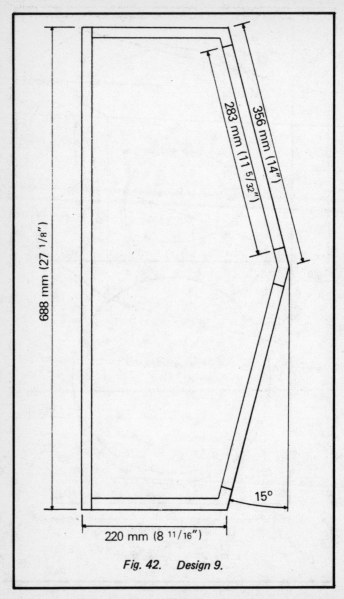

688 mm (27 1/8")

283 mm (11 5/32")

356 mm (14")

15°

220 mm (8 11/16")

Fig. 42.   Design 9.

154

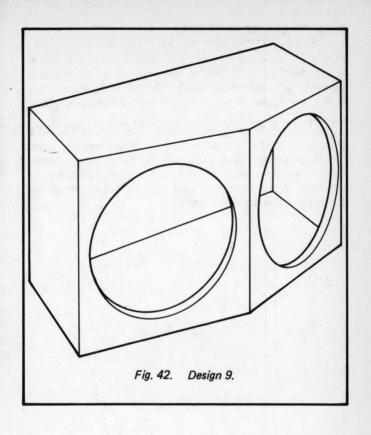

Fig. 42.   Design 9.

Design 10 - Tweeter Box (Fig.43)

As with the mid-range unit, the angles are critical, if anything more so, so these must be measured and cut with care. Joints do not have to be airtight in this case, nor is any wadding required. The drivers are the RTT50 h.f. units which singly have a 70° dispersion angle but in this configuration radiate over 100°.

Like the HF 50, they are available with an X suffix which denotes an internal crossover circuit. With these the crossover frequency is 2 kHz, and they make a convenient complement to any bass unit. If used with a mid-range driver the non-suffix model should be used with a three-way crossover circuit to supply the whole system.

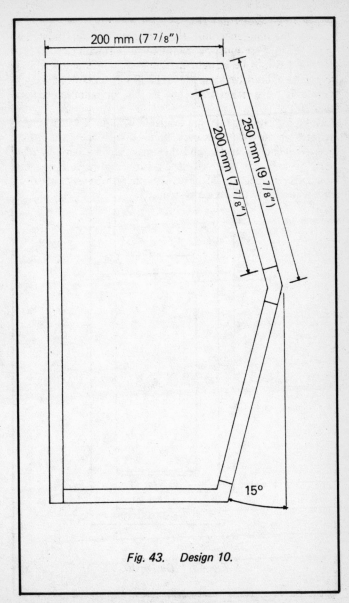

200 mm (7 7/8")

250 mm (9 7/8")

200 mm (7 7/8")

15°

Fig. 43.   Design 10.

157

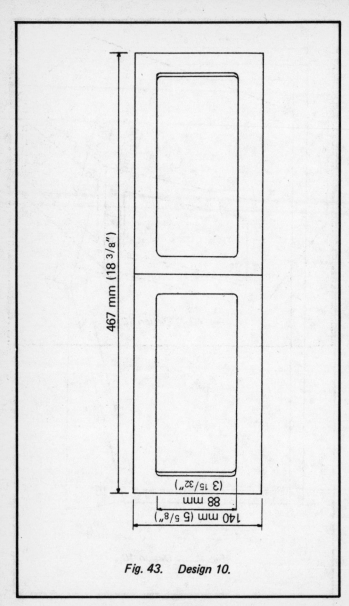

467 mm (18 3/8")

88 mm
(3 15/32")

140 mm (5 5/8")

Fig. 43.   Design 10.

158

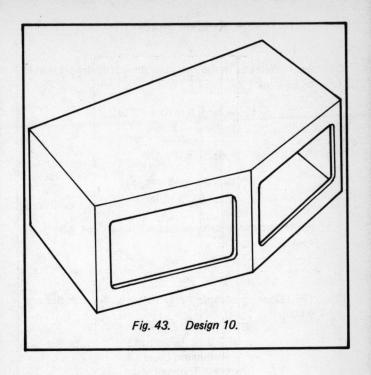

Fig. 43.   Design 10.

Readers' Notes

(1)   Any queries as to the enclosure designs or drivers should be addressed to:

Celestion International Ltd.,
Foxhall Road,
Ipswich,
Suffolk IP3 8JP

Telephone: 0473 723131
Fax: 0473 729662

Please enclose a stamped addressed envelope with your enquiry.

(2)   The following company may be useful for supplies and materials:

Wilmslow Audio Ltd.,
Wellington Close,
Parkgate Trading Estate,
Knutsford,
Cheshire WA16 8DX

Telephone: 0565 50605

Index

WHAT PEOPLE ARE SAYING ABOUT
THE KAPELLMEISTER SPEAKERS

* " . . . *extraordinary clarity of these speakers.*"

* "*they fulfil the parameters you have set, particularly in the small room I have to use.*"

* "*I was absolutely delighted with the result. The sound is comparable with speakers I sell around £2,000 per pair.*" *(Hi-fi dealer)*

* " . . . *everyone I know have been very impressed with the results.*"

* "*Congratulations on a clever bit of lateral thinking!*"

* "*Frankly I haven't found anything industry has to offer even as remotely as pleasing as the Kapellmeisters.*"

These are some of the comments received from readers who have built the Kapellmeister speakers described in the book *"An Introduction to Loudspeakers and Enclosure Design"* by Vivian Capel. The speakers occupy only 8 inches by 11 inches of floor space, should cost less than £50 the pair, require only modest DIY skills to build, and as readers keep telling us, out-perform very expensive commercial units.

The design is not just another speaker-in-a-box, but an innovatory application of the transmission line principle that overcomes many of the drawbacks of this otherwise excellent type of enclosure.

The book fully describes the theory behind the design and gives full practical instructions on how to build them. It also explains pros and cons and design theory of most other types of enclosure and cross-over networks. A must for all hi-fi enthusiasts, but especially for those interested in acquiring a pair of top-class speakers at moderate cost.

BP256 - AN INTRODUCTION TO LOUDSPEAKERS AND ENCLOSURE DESIGN.
V. CAPEL **£2.95**
0 85934 201 8 *1988* *178 x 111mm* *160 pages*